FRESH-AIR POULTRY HOUSES

The Classic Guide to Open-Front Chicken Coops For Healthier Poultry

by Prince T. Woods, M.D.

Norton Creek Press
http://www.nortoncreekpress.com

Fresh-Air Poultry Houses
The Classic Guide to Open-Front Chicken Coops
for Healthier Poultry

by Prince T. Woods M.D.

Originally printed in 1924 as "Modern Fresh-Air Poultry Houses."

ISBN 978-0-9721770-6-1

Norton Creek Press
36475 Norton Creek Road
Blodgett, Oregon 97326

http://www.nortoncreekpress.com

INTRODUCTION

To stay healthy, your chickens need plenty of ventilation-probably more than they're getting today. This was discovered over 100 years ago, but has been largely forgotten. Today's small-flock housing tends to be dank, dark, and smelly. Chickens, like miners' canaries, are easily harmed by poor air quality. Wet litter breeds disease. Darkness forces chickens, like parrots, to be artificially inactive. "Dank, dark, and smelly" is a deadly combination!

Closed chicken houses are so harmful that knocking out a wall can cause an immediate improvement, even in winter. Chickens, after all, have a thick coat of feathers to keep them warm, but are vulnerable to poor air quality and pathogens in the litter; and their unwillingness to eat in the dark means they can starve in the midst of plenty.

Fresh-Air Poultry Houses was written by Dr. Prince T. Woods, a noted poultry health expert. Dr. Woods describes not only his own poultry houses, but those of many of his clients, giving the book a breadth of experience that makes it a unique resource. This 1924 book is old-fashioned and a little eccentric, but in a good way.

There are plenty of photographs, plus drawings showing the framing of each house, with construction notes in the text. He does not give the dimensions of every piece of wood, however, or provide lists of materials; you'll have to figure these out for yourself. But it's not hard. Knowing what you're doing and why is the hard part, and this book will tell you that.

This book was written before modern materials like plywood or metal roofing, but you will find that this hardly matters. *Fresh-Air Poultry Houses* tells you what good chicken-house are all about. Any modern introduction to building techniques will bring you up to speed on materials. So by the time you've read two books, you'll have the best of both worlds, and a better knowledge of the whys and wherefores of chicken-house construction than practically anyone who hasn't been dead for fifty years.

Modern Fresh Air Poultry Houses is a good example of the Norton Creek Press motto: "Most of the best books are out of print and forgotten, but we can fix that!" Check out our other offerings on http://www.nortoncreekpress.com.

Robert Plamondon
October, 2008

FOREWORD

This book was written to review personal experience with fresh-air houses for poultry, and observations of results secured by others, extending over a considerable number of years, and to preserve certain notes on open-air living, with the hope that what is set forth herein may prove helpful to all lovers of good poultry.

These chapters were originally prepared as a series of articles on "Modern Fresh-Air Poultry Houses, a New Series on Common Sense Housing of Poultry" and published in The Poultry Item, Sellersville, Penna. There is so much interest in open-air living for both man and fowls, in modern fresh-air methods, and so many readers have expressed a desire to have this series "all between two covers," that the publishers are now presenting this book to meet the demand.

The plans and instructions for building poultry houses and equipment contained herein should prove sufficiently plain and easy to understand to enable even a novice at carpentery to build the houses recommended. With a little patience the reader can work out for himself all the specifications necessary, to suit available building material, from the plans and dimensions given, using a home-made paper scale as described in the text.

Special instructions, other plans, blue prints, or other specifications are not available and CANNOT be supplied. So, please do not ask for them. Anyone who has had a little experience in the use of carpenter's tools should be able to take the plans here given and build a good poultry house by following instructions. There is nothing difficult about it and very little skill is required. **Read carefully, and read it all.** All of the information really necessary will be found in these chapters.

Fresh-air poultry houses have been thoroly tested. They have come to stay. The adoption of open-front houses and modern fresh-air methods mean better poultry and better results. If this little book helps a bit in the good cause, gains recruits to the modern method of fresh-air or open-air living for Mankind and domesticated poultry, the work of preparing it will have proved well worth while.

June, 1924.   **The Author.**

Contents

CHAPTER I

Benefits of Fresh-Air Plan—Early Types of Fresh-Air Houses

"He who lives after Nature, shall never be poor; after opinion, shall never be rich."—Lucius Annaeus Seneca.

BEFORE entering into the discussion of several good types of fresh-air houses in detail, with suggestions concerning construction, I am presenting some interesting data on the fresh-air plan and benefits to be secured.

Everybody may believe in fresh air, but in actual practice many seem to fear both fresh air and sunlight, at least they fail to make good use of these great blessings so freely bestowed upon us.

There are many more advocates of fresh air today than there were 25 years ago, but sometimes it seems as if most of us are lacking in appreciation of the good things we can secure without cost. If fresh air and sunshine, instead of being free to all, were delivered by meter and charged for at high rates, both would be in greater demand and much more appreciated. There are many among us who have to see a price tag before we can appreciate values.

Altho open-air living and the fresh-air housing plan, for both man and domestic animals, insure better health, more power to resist disease and increase efficiency, the truth told by Dr. Oliver Wendell Holmes, many years ago, aptly applies today:

"God lent His creatures light and air, and waters open to the skies; Man locks him in a stifling lair and wonders why his brother dies."

It is pretty well known that when so-called uncivilized naked savages, who live in the open, are taught to wear clothes, live in closed houses and adopt other habits of civilized white men, they soon sicken and die of "white man's diseases," often of tuberculosis. The story is told of 25 years of hard fighting by a great civilized nation to control a small tribe of naked savages, without success. Finally the troops were called off and one unarmed man attempted to do by peaceful means what large armies had failed to accomplish. He was successful. In a short time he won the confidence of the natives and induced them to make peace and to occupy a reservation where they were provided with houses and clothing and otherwise "civilized." In a few years only a handful of the once strong tribe remained alive. Some of these lingered to die of old age and the tribe is now extinct.

Open-Air Sleeping-Porches

Slowly we are learning that living as much as possible in the open-air and the use of fresh-air sleeping quarters, both summer and winter, not only cure but prevent diseases. Open-air sleeping-porches are much more common today than they were a dozen years ago, but too few houses are provided with this essential for right living.

An interesting article by A. O. Neal, Registrar of the University of Arizona, Tuscon, in "The Nation's Health," tells that it is obligatory for all students who live on the college grounds, to sleep in the open air. All dormitories are provided with open-air sleeping-porches. Both men and women students are required to sleep outside of their study rooms on open-front porches. Canvas curtains are provided for use in case of driving storms. Any students who cannot or will not adjust themselves to sleeping in the open air, must find quarters outside the campus or in the infirmary. Study rooms, which open onto the sleeping porches, are provided with all modern conveniences and steam heat. For twenty-three years this fresh-air plan has proved satisfactory. Students make extraordinary gains in weight and endurance in a remarkably short time. The benefits of rest and sleep in the open are shown also in greater vitality, increased efficiency and better work.

Here in the variable climate of Eastern Massachusetts, often bleak, blustery and very cold in winter, my own family have used an open-air sleeping-porch, with wire screen front, on the south side of our house, both summer and winter for the last ten years. The results have been entirely satisfactory and some of our neighbors have followed our example.

Our poultry has been housed in fresh-air open-front houses almost exclusively, except a few flocks for experimental purposes, for twenty years. The only fair way to test any new plan is to try it out side by side with the old one under the same conditions. At first we used the common closed houses, then modified closed houses, and finally entirely open-front houses. These last were tried out side by side with closed houses for several seasons, with the result that we finally discarded the closed type.

"Fresh Air and Bad Air"

About a dozen years ago, J. P. Muller, one-time lieutenant in the Danish army and later inspector to the Vejlefjord Sanatorium, published a very interesting and instructive little volume entitled "The Fresh Air Book." It deals with open-air living and sleeping, air and sun baths, general hygiene, what to wear and how to exercise, and it is well worth while to anyone interested in living and the enjoyment of good health. Here are some extracts from a chapter on "Fresh Air and Bad Air," including a discussion of "drafts":

"Nearly everyone is agreed today that sickness and short life are the consequences of unnatural and unhealthful modes of living. All are confirmed in the belief that fresh air is an all-powerful source of health, and that bad air, on the other hand, is exceedingly harmful, even dangerous. These things are common knowledge, but how uncommon it is to find practice in accordance with the knowledge. The vast majority of people live in bad air. That celebrated savants and erudite hygienists are no exception to this rule, I have had occasion to prove. Some little while ago, at a congress in Liege, thruout an entire week, some two hundred hygienists of all nations sat in a hall of the University in which not the slightest trace of artificial or natur-

Fig. 1—Open-Front Poultry House with Monitor-top Ventilator. Built about 1852—Maryland.

al ventilation was to be found. The hall, moreover, was covered by a large glass roof. * * * * * I tried once to let a little air into the hall by opening a door in the rear, some half hour before the proceedings commenced; but, five minutes later, a very much laced-in and black-clothed woman, also a hygienist, appeared and closed the door. Another day I opened at least ten times a side door that led to the vestibule, but it was always re-shut by servants. At last I declined to stay in the hall and tried to follow the proceedings from without as best I could. If I did not protest at once against the dreadful air in the hall it was because I took a great 'scientific' interest in finding out if an assembly of learned people would really sit for a number of days in such an atmosphere. In that place, where the air grew every day closer, thicker, fouler and more stinking, the assembled hygienists remained; many of them looked pale and unhealthy, and several sat in their overcoats and hats, altho it was mild, late summer weather."

(Compare this with your own experience at recent conventions, places of amusement, or on trains. If it is true that everybody believes in fresh air, why do so many seem afraid of it?—P. T. W.)

"When such things happen at the fountain heads of physical wisdom, so to speak, is it to be wondered at that the public has no practical understanding of the value of good air? Good air—be it cold or warm—is the foundation of all conditions of life; bad air—cold or warm—is, everywhere, the most powerful and common cause of sickness and short life. * * * * *

"In an enclosed room, filled with warm, poisonous air, a healthy body is susceptible to reaction in a moment, and will feel ill; whereas a body accustomed to impure air will not be in the least affected, quietly absorbing one poison after the other, until the day of the inevitable hygienic crash comes. It is by no means necessary that the warm air in a room be stale. * * * * *

Fear of Drafts

"Many people have an actual and sickly fear of draft, and in their endeavor to escape the harmful consequences of a draft they often avail themselves of a wrong medium. The more one puts one's self in a stove and the more one shuts one's self in, the more harmful is the draft, if, in spite of all precautions, it happens to gain an entrance at some tiny hole or other. Draft is caused, as is known, by the great difference of temperature between the inner and outer atmosphere. Cold air can easily stream in thru the keyhole, unfastened windows, open doors, and so forth. Should such a fine streak of air unluckily strike an isolated spot on an overheated and sensitive human body, it would cause cold or rheumatism. The same thing happens in event of anyone going from a lengthened sojourn in an overheated room out into the cold. Rather should the rooms be thrown open so that the difference of temperature outside and inside is not too great.

"Then the air may blow thru the large windows and doors, and if the occupants be well clad, it will be of more benefit than harm. Wind is not draft. We should protect ourselves against the thin, cold stream and take care not to leave a very hot room to go out into the cold air.

"People often have a remarkable horror of sleeping with the windows open, altho it ought to be well understood that it is as necessary to inhale fresh air while asleep as when at one's daily work. Many people regard night air as something mysterious and dangerous. If that were the case, how would wild animals and birds be able to protect themselves? At times I have encountered the superstition that blindness is caused by sleeping near an open window, while others labor under the absurd delusion that deafness results therefrom!

"During the four and a half years that I was inspector to the Vejlefjord Sanatorium, I saw to it that the more than a thousand patients had the windows of their bedrooms wide open, even during storms and the depth of winter. As one entered the room from the corridor, it often seemed like emerging from a warm room into an iced one. That a great number of these patients had their lives virtually restored to them was due to this day and night inhalation of fresh air. I never heard of a single case of earache or eye trouble among them. * * * * *

Fig. 2—Open-Front Poultry Houses in Winter on Village Experimental Plant—Massachusetts.

"If the air be artificially warmed, that is by a stove, it can, owing to its high temperature, even if it were originally pure, of itself prove a disadvantage, because it enervates those who inhale it, and makes them keenly sensitive to cold, owing to the great difference between the air outside and inside. A healthy body that, by means of a powerful skin activity, provides a lively exchange of matter, and possesses 'well-trained' blood corpuscles—conditions by which we may be able to withstand attacks of sickness—will revolt at once against too much artificial warmth."

The author calls attention in detail to the dangers attendant upon so-called "airing out" and "ventilation" of close rooms or apartments, as generally practiced, and refers to such procedure as "frightful air agitations" to be avoided. He recommends daily air baths and sun baths whenever possible and says: "Fresh air being not only the preventive, but also the cure, of most diseases, it is surely the most powerful factor in promoting longevity."

I have quoted thus at length from Lt. Muller because he emphasizes certain points in regard to fresh-air methods which apply quite as well to the care of poultry as they do to the well-being of the human body. It is largely on these same points that some "constitutional objectors" to fresh-air poultry keeping are continually taking issue.

Made to Live in The Open

Nature made fowls to live in the open. She provided cock and hen with generous garments of feathers; arranged for constant replacement and repair, heavier underfluff of soft warm down for cold weather wear, a complete new outfit at least once a year, nearly perfect protection against both heat and cold as well as from storms. Housing them is an artificial condition wholly for Man's convenience and chiefly essential for comfort in care and management and protection against thieves both two and four legged.

Some contend that in the beginning fowls were of tropical origin and therefore in cold climates should be closely housed. Be that as it may, and it has not been proved beyond a doubt, fowls, both wild and domestic, have been pretty widely and generally distributed thru all climates wherever man is found, to the limit of the timber line and beyond. For several thousand years the domestic cock and hen have been acclimated wherever man lives and makes his home, be the country cold, temperate or hot. Most of us can recall or know of farm flocks that roost in the trees, even in winter. Evidently in Robert Burns' day, Scotch poultry slept in the open from this bit of "A Winter Night"—

> "I heard nae maer, for Chanticleer
>   Shook off the pouthery snaw,
> And hailed the morning with a cheer,
>   A cottage rousing craw."

If it were not for foxes, owls, large hawks, and more particularly, modern chicken thieves with auto-trucks, I should yet be keeping a good sized flock of fowls in a pine grove, without house of any sort, roosting in the trees, protected only by the thick growth of white pines, a five foot wire fence, and provided with covered nests and feed hoppers. I tried the plan when we first moved on this farm, before the pine timber was cleared of dead branches and undergrowth. For several seasons this houseless poultry keeping worked well, even the foxes and owls were not very troublesome, but with the great increase of auto traffic came clever thieves from town, and now, if one wants to keep anything on the farm he must lock it up securely under cover or stand guard over it with a shot gun. These out-door birds had wonderful plumage with a fine sheen and were splendid layers. No sickness in flock.

Consider the Titmouse

Whenever disposed to fear the effect of cold fresh air, properly provided for, upon our well-clothed domestic poultry, consider the titmouse, that tiny atom of bird life which in zero weather flits about from bough to twig in our snow-clad trees cheerfully calling, "Chic-a-deedee." If these tiny bits of blood, bone, skin and feathers can weather our winter storms in the open, why worry about well-clad fowls in a well-built open-front house?

Read Ralph Waldo Emerson's poem, "The Titmouse." The poet "chilled wading in the snow-choked wood" was concerned over the long tramp home in the cold:

"When piped a tiny voice hard by,
Gay and polite, a cheerful cry,
Chic-chicadeedee! saucy note
Out of sound heart and merry throat,
As if it said, 'Good day, good sir!
Fine afternoon, old passenger!
Happy to meet you in these places,
Where January brings few faces.'
 * * * * * *

"Flew near, with soft wing grazed my hand,
Hopped on the bough, then, darting low,
Prints his small impress on the snow,
Shows feats of his gymnastic play,
Head downward, clinging to the spray.

"Here was this atom in full breath,
Hurling defiance at vast death;
This scrap of valor just for play
Fronts the north-wind in waistcoat gray,
As if to shame my weak behavior;
 * * * * * *

"What fire burns in that little chest
So frolic, stout, and self-possesst?

Henceforth I wear no stripe but thine;
Ashes and jet all hues outshine.
Why are not diamonds black and gray,
To ape thy dare-devil array?
And I affirm, the spacious North
Exists to draw thy virtue forth.
I think no virtue goes with size;
The reason of all cowardice
Is, that men are overgrown,
And, to be valiant, must come down
To the titmouse dimension!

" 'Tis good-will makes intelligence,
And I began to catch the sense
Of my bird's song: 'Live out of doors
In the great woods, on prairie floors.
I dine in the sun; when he sinks in the sea,
I too have a hole in a hollow tree;
And I like less when Summer beats
With stifling beams on these retreats,
Than noontide twilights which snow makes
With tempest of the blinding flakes.
For well the soul, if stout within,
Can arm impregnably the skin;
And polar frost my frame defied,
Made of the air that blows outside.' "

Opposition to Open-Front Houses

Recently I have read several articles, by as many authors, in which the open-front fresh-air poultry house is severely condemned and a return to closed houses and even artificially heated houses advised for breeding and laying stock. Prejudice dies hard. When the bathtub and other modern toilet conveniences were first introduced there was a hue and cry against them, even a good many able physicians protested against bathtubs and frequent bathing and predicted dire calamity as the result of general use of such inventions. From reading these opposition articles I believe that these authors really know next to nothing about open-air houses or their practical use.

I do not look for any return to closed or heated houses for breeding fowls and laying stock. It is not so very long ago that I visited a plant where the fowls were housed in an expensively built, plastered, and hot-water heated building, and a deep pit provided in an out-of-the-way part of the farm for burial of many birds dead from roup. I have been called in many such cases to suggest a remedy for the trouble. In every case opening the front of the building, thoro disinfection, and discontinuance of the artificial heat, effected a cure. On one

plant, in winter weather with the thermometer at 20 degrees below zero, conditions were so bad that the fowls were taken from the house and placed in small open-front colony coops, in hope that the fittest might survive. To the surprise of the owner this severe and, as he thought, "cruel" treatment resulted in saving the majority of the flock, including some valuable exhibition specimens.

Fig. 3—Common type of Portable Colony House used on Rhode Island Shore Farms.

Altho open-front poultry houses have been quite vigorously boosted during the past twenty years and in one type or another, were in use long before that, there has been very little complaint from open-front house users. Such complaint as has come to my personal attention has been chiefly from persons who have modified original plans with features of their own design, or have added curtains and screens of various sizes and sorts to partially shut in the open front or to "protect" the roosts.

Some few good open-air poultry houses are provided with screens to partially close the front and these will be described later; but in the open-front house of my own plan, as used on my own farm and on the one I previously owned, no curtains of any sort are used. Frequently the curtain or screen may defeat the purpose of the open front.

The open-front fresh-air poultry house is really a very simple affair and the simpler the construction the better, as a rule. The essentials are an open-front that always stays open, protected by wire screen and overhanging eaves from driving storms of rain or snow, ample floor space, opportunity for sunlight to reach most parts of the house during some part of the day, tight roof, sides and back, comfortable roosts, simple furnishings and a good floor. The house should have good depth so that roosts are well back from the open front.

I am firmly convinced that anyone who cannot get good results with an open-front house either has failed to build the house properly or is himself, in large measure, at fault.

Some Benefits of Open-Front Housing

Not the least among the benefits of open-air housing of poultry is that the operator does not need to worry about ventilation, opening and shutting slides, shutters, curtains, windows and doors almost

Fig. 4—Hip-roof Closed House of Undesirable type. Hot in Summer. Damp and cold in Winter.

continuously, in an effort to make adjustments to suit weather conditions.

There is less dampness in the open-front house, the air is dryer and there is greater opportunity for dust to escape.

Fowls enjoy better health, are more comfortable, are less affected by weather changes. The egg yield is generally better and more uniform. Better health and lessened liability to disease result in better fertility and better hatches of strong chicks.

I have had no cases of frosted toes in open-front houses altho there were a few such, one winter, in a closed house. Frosted combs and wattles are less common than in closed houses. Such frosting is commonly the result of getting comb and wattles wet with drinking water or from exposure to cold wind after close confinement, rather than a matter of extreme cold alone. Have wintered a cock and four hens, single comb variety, in a large 20x20 ft. open-front house, with some extremely severe below zero weather and not one touch of frost-bite. Condition has much to do with power to resist cold and fowls are in better condition in open-air quarters.

Fresh-air fowls have better appetites, do not need to have their days lengthened by artificial light in order to get maximum egg pro-duction.

"Sleep is Nature's sweet restorer." Building up, repair and rejuv-enation of the body tissues occur during rest and sleep. During the day the body is busy producing energy in the form of work and heat.

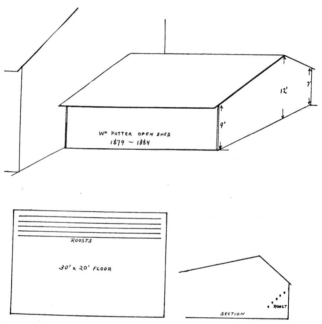

Fig. 5—Large Open-Front Poultry House attached to East Side of barn. Built for wagon shed. Remodeled for poultry 1879—Massachusetts.

In cold weather, particularly, we do not care to shorten the hen's hours of rest; we prefer to have her make a good job of it and come off the roost ready to hustle and do a good big day's work during the short hours of daylight.

The hen carries a much higher normal temperature than human beings and breathes much more rapidly. She requires for her well-being an abundance of oxygen in fresh air. She needs fresh air at night even more than by day. The open-front house supplies this need safely and conveniently.

As fowls cannot lay aside their overcoats, or heavy feathers garments, at will, they are far more comfortable in open-front houses than in closed ones.

Various Types

I have not been able to learn who built the first open-air poultry house and probably it dates a very long way back in the history of the domestication of poultry. One of the earliest types of open-front house which I have seen was built on a Maryland farm about 1852 and was still in good condition and in use when I photographed it a few years ago. This is shown in Fig. 1, and is a large and rather expensive house, with a monitor top fitted with adjustable ventilating blinds. It was built on a foundation of cut granite. The house is about 14x24 ft., 11 ft. high from base of sill to eaves, full double sash window in each end and one behind each large door, two large "barn doors" in front, each 9x6 ft.

The winter scene in Fig. 2, shows a group of open-front poultry houses which I used for experimental purposes when living in a Northern Massachusetts village about fifteen years ago. Fig. 3 is a common type of closed colony house in use on Rhode Island shore farms. It is a good house of its kind, about 8x10 ft. built of common boards with cracks battened and roof shingled. It is generally operated with door and window wide open and from dawn until dark the flock has free range on beach and field. Even with door and window closed this house is not tight and leaks air on all sides. When asked about "drafts" the owner said: "Drafts used to worry me at the start, but now I never think about them. If the hen on the roost feels air blowing on her and hasn't sense enough to turn about and face it so that it won't get under her feathers, she isn't worth her keep." Some of these houses have board floors, some have none, and when the earth floor gets foul the house is moved to a fresh location.

The low hip-roofed closed house shown in Fig. 4, is an undesirable type. Buildings of this sort accumulate foul air, get overheated in summer and on sunny days in winter and are cold on winter nights and cloudy days. Such houses are damp and smelly and decidedly chilly in cold weather. Replacing the front windows with fine wire netting would make a decided improvement in it.

The first time I ever saw fowls housed in an open-front shed was about 1879, as near as I can recall, on the farm of William Potter, Salem, Mass. There were a good many farms in our neighborhood where fowls roosted in the trees, but it so happened that on the Potter farm an old wagon shed, attached to the east side of the barn, had been converted into poultry quarters. This shed had a short reach of roof to the north and a long reach, with overhanging eaves, to the

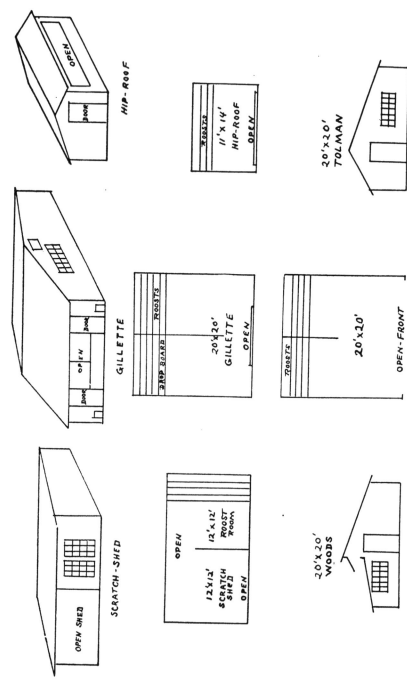

Fig. 6.—Outline diagram of Five Open-Front Poultry Houses of Different types. The more popular ones will be described in detail in later chapters.

south. It was about 30 ft. wide by 20 ft. deep, 9 ft. stud at front, 12 ft. at peak and 7 ft. high at rear. Roosts were arranged at the rear in the old style "poultry ladder," low in front and high next rear wall. Between '79 and '84 I spent a good deal of time on that farm and, as I remember it, that open-front shed made a mighty fine poultry house. Fig. 5 shows elevation, end section and ground plan of this open-front shed.

A group diagram showing elevation and floor plan of various types of open-front houses is shown in Fig. 6. The more desirable of these houses will be treated in detail in other chapters to follow. Colony houses and long continuous houses will be described and discussed. Location, foundations, floors, building materials, construction and plans for modern fresh-air houses, necessary furnishings, etc. will be considered in detail so that anyone with skill in handling carpenter's tools should be able to build.

"HAVE CONFIDENCE—One of the first things a beginner with open-front houses needs is to have confidence in the house and the comfort of his flocks. If the house is built right the fowls will be safe and right, no matter wnat the weather may be. Neighbors will criticizs and make dire predictions; this is an ancient right of neighborly privilege and custom. Forget it! Those who come to scoff usually remain to believe and become open-front house users. Have confidence; don't get cold feet."—Dr. P. T. Woods in "Rural New-Yorker," 1924.

CHAPTER II

Joseph Tolman's Experience—Notes on Location— Foundation—Floors—Building Materials

"The slaves of custom and established mode,
With pack-horse constancy we keep the road
Crooked or straight, thru quags or thorny dells,
True to the jingling of our leader's bells."   —Cowper

FOR MANY YEARS it was the custom or common usage of poultry keepers to keep fowls in closed houses. Here and there flocks were kept in the open sheds. The majority of folks were inclined to look upon the farmer whose flocks roosted in the trees, or wherever they could find shelter, as shiftless, careless or even "cruel." The advocate of fresh-air poultry keeping and open-front houses was considered unduly radical, a crank, or extremist.

Reviewing the subject of poultry housing for the past quarter of a century and more, the practice and teachings of early advocates of fresh-air poultry keeping seem far from radical when viewed from a present day standpoint. They were conservative and careful to a marked degree. The development of the modern fresh-air house was a slow process and even today we find evidence of fear of drafts and of unnecessary precautions taken for the "protection" of the fowls housed.

If tiny wild birds and feathered game the size of small breeds of domestic poultry, can successfully withstand severe northern winters in our woods with no shelter but trees and brush, why worry about fowls in open-front shelter? Some will say, "but we keep fowls for egg production and for exhibition and must keep them carefully housed to get desired results." Well, some of the most successful exhibitors now use open-front houses and experience of many years has proved that condition and egg yield are better in open-front houses than in closed ones, also that the fresh-air flocks are less affected by weather changes. There is nothing to be gained by keeping fowls under unnatural conditions and the closed type of house that may be a sweat-box by day and a refrigerator by night, certainly provides most unnatural conditions for fowls originally intended for open-air life.

Must Have Fresh Air

Brief study of the anatomy and physiology of fowls will demonstrate that they differ considerably in some important particulars from other domestic animals and that they are very dependent upon a generous supply of fresh air for their well being. Good as fresh air is for men and other mammals, it is even more important and necessary to fowls.

The excellent and wonderfully effective breathing apparatus of fowls differs from other domesticated animals. The lungs are comparatively small and have little elasticity. This is compensated for by free communication with large reservoirs or sacs, nine in number. These sacs are independent of each other and freely communicate with the tubular apparatus, with the lungs and with certain bones. The air sacs serve to feed air to the lungs between periods of inspiration. Some oxygenation of the blood may take place thru the walls of the sacs as well as in the lungs. The air sacs also serve to diminish the weight of the body and to render equilibrium more stable.

Fowls have no sweat glands so that very little moisture is evaporated from the external surface of the body. Very little heat is lost thru the skin because of the efficient insulation afforded by the feathers. Also the body is unusually well protected from cold and weather. The kidneys excrete only a very small quantity of water. Nearly all the moisture which escapes from the fowl's body is passed off thru the respiratory apparatus.

It should be plain enough to everyone that an abundance of fresh air at all times is necessary to the well-being of fowls—they must have fresh air. They live fast, have a very active respiratory apparatus, breathe rapidly, require much oxygen for the blood to maintain the normal high temperature, and exhale large quantities of carbonic acid and moisture.

Cause of Damp Houses

Much of the dampness in poultry houses, so-called "house sweating," is due to the moisture exhaled by the fowls which condenses on the roof boards, ceiling and walls. When this "house sweating" is excessive it is a certain indication that there is not sufficient ventilation or the house is crowded beyond its capacity. Damp, stale air, lacking in oxygen and carrying an excessive amount of carbonic acid, is a common starting point of poultry diseases in closed houses. The fowl is starved for oxygen and her natural power of resistance to disease is weakened or broken down.

The open-front fresh-air building is a practically dry house as it permits free escape of excess moisture, unless roof boards are too close to roosts when a certain amount of moisture is sure to condense on roof boards above roosts and under some conditions may condense on windows in form of frost. The open-front house gives a full and abundant supply of fresh air, with its contained oxygen, all the time. The fresh air supply is particularly important at night to provide for the heavy demands of the sleeping fowls for life-giving, life-supporting oxygen. Fresh air at night is absolutely necessary to provide for normal restorative processes and the maintenance of body heat during sleep. It has been estimated that fully 60% of the total oxygen needed by the body in the 24 hours is required at night.

Joseph Tolman's Experience

Joseph Tolman, successful baby chick man and proprietor of the big fresh-air poultry plant, Rockland, Mass., recited his fresh-air experience in a lecture given before the Springfield Poultry and Pet Stock Association some years ago. A few extracts from this lecture will prove of interest here before we close the introductory matter of this chapter and go on with house construction:—

"When we stop to think of the closed houses that some, yes, the majority of poultrymen have used for their poultry, we should not be surprised that such diseases as roup, diphtheria, cholera, etc., have developed in these closed-house flocks. It is a fact that breeding fowls have been so weakened thru insufficient fresh air, particularly at night, that it has been almost impossible to raise their chicks.

"The first eight years of my work in the poultry business were with the closed type of house, and I met with very poor results. It was no uncommon thing for me to take hatch after hatch out of my incubators, placing them in the brooder, and in less than three weeks carry them out in pails and bags, losing practically the whole hatch, for those that lived were very poor specimens. Perhaps these poor results cannot be wholly attributed to the manner of housing, yet, from results I have obtained since using my fresh-air houses, I am convinced that most of the trouble was due to close-housing my breeding stock.

"My first open-front or fresh-air houses were used during that severe cold winter of 1904 and 1905, and remarkably good results were obtained. Perhaps it will be of interest to you to know what led me to develop my fresh-air poultry house.

"During the spring of 1903, Dr. Prince T. Woods, the well known writer and authority on poultry and poultry diseases, visited a number of poultry plants in our section of the country, where at that time very unsatisfactory results were being obtained. Post-mortem exam-

inations made on a great many birds of various ages led him to believe that an abundance of fresh air in the poultry houses was practically all that was needed to check the disease and put the stock in
better condition. Acting upon his advice, I took the windows out of
my poultry houses at once and kept them out until late fall. Seeing
a marked change in the health and vigor of my birds, and knowing of
the remarkable results being obtained in many sections of the country
in the sanitariums that are provided with outdoor sleeping rooms for
patients, I felt that in order to get the best results with my breeders I
needed to keep the windows wide open all winter. This was the winter of 1903 and 1904.

Fig. 7—Tolman Houses in Winter, Author's Village Experimental
Plant—Massachusetts.

"Altho the three houses that I kept my breeders in were not well
adapted to such exposure to the elements in severe winter weather, I
obtained fine results, receiving an egg yield during the coldest months,
from 150 Light Brahmas, of from 50 to 60 per cent. I was able to
hatch from 55 to 65 per cent of the total number of eggs placed in the
incubators, and the chickens were large, strong and vigorous. The
following spring I had a very small death rate among my chickens.

"The three houses with which I made this test were 20x10, (20 ft.
long, 10 ft. deep), pitch roof, 5 ft. post, two windows in the south side.
During a heavy snow storm, if the wind blew, the floor of the house
would be entirely covered with snow, and a large drift in front unless
one of the windows was closed. I decided the following fall to try to
overcome this defect as much as possible, and I believe with my improved fresh-air house I have controlled the effects of the weather
changes as much as it is possible to with a house that is open all the
time.

"I will tell you of an experience with a snow storm I had with
these old style houses run with windows open. It was during the first

severe snow storm of the year, about the last of December. At night when I left my houses the weather was calm, but cloudy. I did not expect a storm, so left the four windows wide open as usual. About midnight I awoke and found it was blowing almost a gale and snowing hard. In the morning the snow was a foot deep and had drifted badly. It had also grown quite cold. When I arrived at my houses to water and feed the fowls, I found the entire floor of the houses was covered with snow and opposite the windows it lay in drifts two and three feet deep. There was also quite a little snow on the dropping boards. I wondered what effect this would have upon the egg yield, but found after the eggs were gathered that I had more than any previous day, and from this time on they increased right along. I did not have a single bird catch cold or experience any other setback from this extreme exposure. * * * * *

"To illustrate the benefit of fresh air in such diseases as roup, colds, etc., I will quote what Prof. W. P. Brooks Hatch Experiment Station, Mass., wrote me:—'We are becoming more and more convinced that plenty of fresh air both night and day is favorable to health and satisfactory egg production. Last winter I kept a small number of fowls in an open coop on the ground all winter long. They were protected simply by putting burlap over the wire mesh around the sides of that portion of the coop at one end covered by a light roof of building paper. Under this roof were the perches. This was certainly extreme treatment. The fowls were put there because they showed signs of roup and two of them lost an eye each, but they recovered in a short time and the hens began to lay in mid-winter, almost literally while living in a snow bank!' * * * * *

"Prof. Charles K. Graham, of Connecticut Agricultural College, Storrs, made a test in a common tent of the A type. Leaving the front open in this tent, he installed a flock of White Leghorn fowls headed by a proud, handsome cock bird, and found that not a comb was frosted, while some of the combs in the regulation closed houses were touched with frost."

The lecture from which above is quoted was delivered in May, 1908. Since that time Mr. Tolman has given up Light Brahmas and the soft-roaster business and gone in for White Plymouth Rocks, custom hatching and day old chicks. He has prospered and built up a big, successful business. Before I gave up White Rocks to go into Black Langshans exclusively, I used to buy baby chicks of Tolman, from time to time, and so am in a position to know from personal experience that his fresh air flocks produced strong sturdy chicks. His plant was one of the few to carry on at close to full capacity during the difficult war times. Comparing the Tolman fresh-air house—a type which he developed in the fall of 1904—with closed houses, Mr Tolman said:—

"Those who use the Tolman fresh-air house will find the house very comfortable in winter in comparison with the old style closed poultry buildings. Dampness never gathers. The walls are always dry, owing to the fact that the front is open at all times. The air is alive and fresh, not dead and foul, there is no chilling dampness, and the fowls enjoy comfortable and invigorating pure air night and day. The litter and earth of the floor remain dry and even get dusty. In the winter of 1906, altho the weather was very severe, the water did not seem to freeze any more quickly in this house than it does in those of the closed type altho of course water will freeze in any such building during cold winter weather when the thermometer goes down near zero."

Fig. 8—Radical Fresh-Air Methods in 1904. 10x20 closed house on plant of Joseph Tolman, Rockland, Mass. End knocked out and given a southern exposure to provide an "open-front."

Fig. 7 shows a winter view of two Tolman open-front houses on a village experimental plant formerly owned by the author in the northern part of Essex County, Mass. These houses were built in January, 1906, and used for fowls as soon as built. The measurements as I recall them were 8 ft. wide by 14 ft. deep, 50 inches high in rear and 45 inches in front. A flock of Buff Wyandottes was housed in one and a flock of White Wyandottes in the other. In spite of the fact that the houses were built in mid-winter on frozen ground, in which a pick had to be used to start the post holes, and occupied as soon as built by flocks which had previously been housed in closed buildings, the results were entirely satisfactory, no sickness in either flock and a fine egg yield from the start. The fertility was good, the eggs hatched well and the chicks lived and made splendid specimens. One

Fig. 9—Row of Reconstructed Closed-type houses on Tolman plant. Ends knocked out to supply fresh air day and night. Operated successfully several years. Small closed hip-roof house in background was common type in vicinity. From this the Tolman open-front house was developed by extending the front reach of roof and leaving front of house entirely open.

of the White Wyandotte cockerels hatched from eggs from this flock sold for $50, and was a winner at several local shows in New York state near the Massachusetts line.

Fig. 8 is a view of one of Mr. Tolman's closed type 10x20 ft. houses after he had swung it round end to the south and knocked out part of the end to convert it into an "open-front." The open front is protected by two inch mesh hexagon wire netting only. No curtains of any sort. The roosts are in the north end. It was houses like this, before opening the ends, that Mr. Tolman ran with windows wide open in the winter of 1903, in which the snow from the December storm drifted 3 ft. deep in front of windows and was spread all over the floor and even on the dropping boards. Fig. 9 shows a group of these converted open fronts as operated for several years. Such fresh-air methods were considered radical in 1904 and 1905. The fowls were well protected, more comfortable than in closed houses, enjoyed better health; produced more eggs, gave better fertility and better chicks than the closed house flocks.

Location for Poultry House

Selecting the location for a poultry house is a matter to be governed largely by conditions and convenience. In the case of the back-lotter there is very little choice. He has to locate the house where he can and make the most of whatever sunlight he can get. The country place poultry houses are generally located where convenient of access but at the same time not overly conspicuous, for most summer home owners prefer the poultry quarters somewhat hidden from view.

The proprietor of a commercial or specialty poultry plant will consider convenience and labor saving first, display for advertising purposes second. The location will in some measure depend upon whether the houses are to be of the colony or of the long continuous type.

The man who combines poultry with diversified farming, and has his farm arranged with due regard for rotation of crops, will undoubtedly find the portable type of colony house best suited to his requirements. Such houses permit moving the poultry to new fields, cropping the land run over by the fowls and keeping the soil sweet and productive. This plan generally works out best in the long run.

There are a few important things to remember in locating any poultry house. Keep out of hollows where water settles after a heavy rain. Set the house high and dry where both the land drainage and air drainage are good. If locating on a slight slope or side hill, grade the house site level and a little above ground level at rear of house or high part of slope. Provide for drainage of drip from rear slope of roof and of surface water. A southerly slope is usually best. An easterly or westerly slope can be made good use of if necessary, but a sharp slope to the north, or the north side of a steep hill, is not a good location for a poultry building. On some abrupt south hillsides, if care is taken to make back and side walls water tight and provide for drainage of rain and snow water away from house, it is sometimes a good plan to build into the hillside in half-basement style, providing tight rear and side walls of stone and cement.

As a general rule the house should face south or a little east of south, so that the interior can be well sunned at all seasons.

Whatever house site is selected be sure that drainage of surface water and drip from the eaves is provided. Do not let this water run into the house or under it.

Land that will grow fruit trees and good grass, light loam with gravelly subsoil, is preferable for poultry runs and can be used to good advantage by alternating poultry and crops or for poultry and fruit at the same time. Frequent stirring and cropping of the soil helps to keep it sweet and in good condition for poultry runs.

Heavy land is not so desirable. Sandy, rocky and barren gravelly soils will serve, if necessary, but I would not choose such for best results.

Wet land along running fresh water can be used to advantage for poultry if houses are placed high and dry, but stagnant swamp land is not desirable. If the latter must be used, clear up and drain it first. Salt water marsh makes an excellent poultry run, particularly for free range flocks, if houses are located on dry upland.

With good housing, good food and reasonably good care poultry can be made to do well almost anywhere.

Colony or Long Houses—Which?

My own preference is for colony poultry houses, either permanently located or of portable type. I find them more convenient and

Fig. 10—Two Woods' Open-front Houses on plant of J. W. Parks, Altoona, Pa. These are used for hard coal brooder stoves in chick season and for housing stock when it reaches roosting age.

there is less risk than where all the fowls are kept under one roof in a long house.

There are many poultrymen who prefer a long poultry house. Certain open-front houses are adaptable to the long or continuous type of poultry house, others are not. The one time popular long house with walk or alley in rear is convenient in some ways and undesirable in others. It is expensive to build. Where a long house is used, I consider it better to do away with the walk or alley and provide for pen to pen communication thru house by doors which swing both ways, located about midway between back and front. Passing thru the pens is inconvenient in some ways but it possesses the advantage of bringing the attendant in close contact with the flocks which outweighs any possible disadvantages. To get best results it is necessary to keep in close touch with the birds.

I like small colony houses which can be readily moved about the farm to new locations when desired. There are a number of good portable houses which answer the purpose. Large colony houses should be permanently located and may be arranged in convenient groups. Provision should be made for double yards where possible so that soil can be kept sweet by alternating poultry and crops.

The colony house, which can be used for brooder operation in chicken time, then brooders removed and growing chicks given roosts, later on weeding out and culling flock to leave only the better pullets in the house for fall and winter egg production, provides for year 'round poultry quarters which are very convenient and which possess the considerable advantage of avoiding the troublesome moving about of early pullets, first from brooder or brood coop to growing house and later to laying house. With many growers there are fewer setbacks where chicks spend their first fall and winter in the colony house where they were brooded.

While I was writing the above came a letter from our friend J. W. Parks, proprietor of Wopsy Poultry Yards, Altoona, Penna., home of well known heavy laying Barred Rocks, enclosing a photograph of two of his Woods open-front colony houses, used as brooder houses and as quarters for young stock until matured and disposed of. The letter is reproduced herewith:

Dear Doctor:—

I am enclosing you a couple of prints I had taken lately of two of my Woods type houses.

I am very well pleased with them and they are especially adapted for keeping hard coal brooder stoves in.

Putting roosts in and culling the chicks out from time to time, we get use of the houses the whole year around.

Hope you are meeting with success and thank you for your many past favors, I am,   Your friend,
                                                    J. W. PARKS.

Fig. 10 is view of these Woods houses and chicken runs on the J. W. Parks plant.

Foundations and Floors

Houses intended for small and growing chickens must have rat tight floors of either concrete or wood. It is not safe to use earth floors.

Portable colony houses for adult fowls may be set on a movable foundation of stone, brick, or wooden blocks and earth under house used as floor, filling in a little where necessary or using boards to close space between sills and ground. Providing a clean floor is simply a matter of moving the house to a new site.

For permanent poultry houses, altho I have used such for many years, I consider earth floors the least desirable and most expensive in the long run. Earth floors foul to a considerable depth. It is advisable when such are used to take out the top earth to a depth of at least a foot, or better 18 inches, and refill with fresh earth at least once every year. This is a considerable job and calls for a good deal of labor expense. Too often it is such a nuisance that the work is neglected and the houses are not cleaned out as frequently as they should be.

Tight board floors are excellent if kept clean and made mite proof. In some portable houses I have used a single matched board floor made in sections so that it can be easily removed. For permanent houses a double board floor, well timbered to make it solid, is preferable. Use rough boards snugly laid on floor timbers for first floor. On top of this use smooth matched boards laid at right angles to first course. A layer of asphalt—such as is used for making old roofs water tight, the kind that dries out hard but elastic, about one-quarter of an inch thick will make the floor mite proof and less likely to be gnawed by rats. Crude creosote, or common brown creosote shingle stain, painted on floor boards once a year will make the floor mite proof if asphalt is not desired. Or if neither asphalt nor creosote is desired, sweep clean the board floor and then soak it down with hot whitewash or Carbola disinfecting water-paint applied with a sprayer early in May each year. Select a good warm drying day for the job.

Concrete makes an excellent floor for a permanent poultry building and the directions which follow are quoted from **New England Homestead.** As a rule the top of the concrete floor should be flush with the top of sills. This calls for putting in the floor after foundation walls and sills are laid. It takes a little skill to make a good concrete floor. The sand should be sharp bank sand, the gravel and stones should be clean—free from clay and loam—and well assorted as to size so as to fit in well. The whole must be well mixed and thoroly tamped into place before it begins to set.

"Concrete is one of the best materials you can use for flooring a poultry house. It is rat proof and permanent, and if you lay it properly it will not be damp. In the first place you must provide good drainage. This should be provided for a poultry house no matter what kind of a floor you have. A bed of cinders or gravel 6 to 8 inches thick should be laid as a sub-base for the concrete. The concrete floor itself should be 3½ to 4 inches thick; and a 1-2½-4 mixture of cement, sand and broken stone or pebbles. If you have good clean gravel handy, that is well sorted in size, with some sand in it, you can mix that in proportion of one part of cement to 4 of the gravel. If you make it medium wet and tamp it well you will not need a finishing coat. One of the best ways of finishing a poultry house floor that I have ever seen is to pour a layer of asphalt about ¼ of an inch thick on top of the concrete. This makes the floor warmer, absolutely impervious, and not so hard on the feet of the poultry."—**N. E. Homestead.**

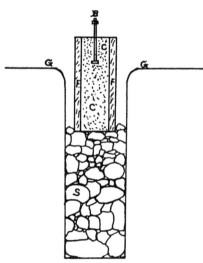

Fig. 11—Section view of foundation trench, sub-base of field stone (S), frame boards for supporting concrete wall (F,F), concrete wall (C,C), anchor bolt for sill (B), G,G, is ground level. After concrete has set, frame boards are removed and trench filled in with earth.

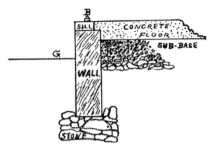

Fig. 12—Section view of concrete foundation wall, concrete floor and sub-base of stone, coarse gravel or cinders. Sill and anchor bolt (B), ground level (G).

For poultry house foundation where a concrete floor is to be laid it is preferable to first make wall on which sills are to rest. Locate house corners and mark them with stakes to which corner boards are fixed at right angles to make corners. With marking line —white fish line will serve—lay out course of sills between corners. Make a good job of it. Along this line of sills dig a trench below frost line, or about 3 ft. deep. For convenience this trench should be about a foot wide. Fill in to within about twelve inches of ground level with large and small stones and coarse gravel or coarse cinders. Above this sub-base the concrete foundation walls should be laid with aid of wood frames 18 inches wide and about 10 ft. long for convenience in handling; should be set firmly in place on sub-base along sill line around entire foundation where wall is to be laid, frames parallel and about six inches apart on inside. Nail corners securely and cleat frames together every three feet to prevent bulging when cement is poured in. The top of frame which is to be top of foundation wall, should be about six inches above ground level. One part of cement to 4 parts of good clean gravel—well assorted as to size and containing some sharp sand—makes a good foundation mixture. Fill in the frames with concrete and level off at top of frame. While filling in the concrete set anchor bolts at corners and ten feet apart upright along the sill line. These bolts should be about 8 inches long and end carrying loose nut should extend about three inches above top of concrete. Sills of 2x4 material laid 4 inch side up are sufficiently

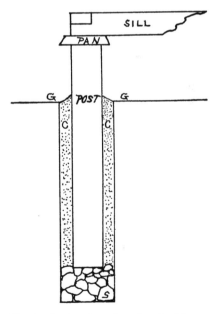

Fig. 13—Section view of wood post set in concrete (C,C), with sub-base or drain of field stone (S). Ground level (G,G). Inverted pan on top of post is to keep rats from working thru floor. Sill joint is shown at house corner.

heavy for use on a concrete foundation. Bore these at proper intervals to receive the bolts. Use a flat washer between sill and nut of bolt to protect sill. Sills should be bolted firmly in place after concrete has hardened. It takes three or four days for concrete to harden sufficiently so that frames may be removed. Sills should be laid flush with outside edge of wall. The frames can be used for laying walls of other houses. It is important to take sufficient time and use care in laying foundation walls and in filling same in with concrete floor. Under ordinary weather conditions the foundation walls will need to season for about two weeks before building begins. Unless walls are well seasoned the weight of house will not be sustained. In hot weather it is well to keep concrete shaded from sun with boards until it is well set.

If a concrete floor is laid with a slight grade, sufficient to run off water, high at rear of house and low in front, and near front graded from sides to center to end at a tile drain covered with a drain cap, it will prove a great convenience. The house can then be washed out with a hose whenever desired. For such a grading job it will be better to call in an expert in concrete work. It is a difficult undertaking for a novice.

The level concrete floor can be washed if necessary with pail and mop, or with a sprayer, and then bailed out with scoop and mop, but a well built drain is a great labor saver.

Concrete posts, provided with anchor bolts of sufficient length to take sills, may be used for houses with wood floors. Make them in frames about 6x8 inches inside measure and set into ground about three feet extending above ground about one foot. Use same mixture and same plan as for wall foundation, except that post holes are dug along sill line about 10 ft. apart to centers. Make them wide enough to work in conveniently. For such houses use a 4x4 or 4x6 sill and have anchor bolts extend far enough above concrete to engage same properly. Use level and line to make sure that tops of posts are on a level, so that when sills are placed the foundation will be level. Let frames for posts remain in place for a week. Do not start house building until posts have seasoned for fifteen days or more.

Sills to be laid in concrete or cement should be given one or more coats of wood-preserving creosote or asphaltum, and same allowed to dry in thoroly before the sills are laid.

Houses with wood floors should have sills fully 12 inches above ground level, and may be placed higher, so that with aid of good dog it is possible to keep space below house free from rats.

Red cedar and locust posts, well seasoned, make the best and most lasting wood posts for house foundation. Wood posts are easily placed and ready to use as soon as set. Post holes for same can be quickly made with a post hole digger. Red cedar posts, in holes three feet deep, hole filled in with a concrete mixture of one part cement, three parts sharp sand and four parts coarse gravel, small stones or cinders, and top of concrete rounded off a little above ground level, will last almost indefinitely.

Seasoned oak posts will serve if cedar or locust cannot be had, but do not last so long. Chestnut also makes a good post.

In preparing for a post foundation, lay out the corners with stakes and guide boards at right angles and make the sill line with cord in same manner as when preparing to dig trench for concrete foundation wall. Level tops of wood posts so that sills are on a level and spike sills to posts.

Fig. 11 shows section view of foundation and concrete wall as laid; G, G, ground level; F, F, frame boards for retaining concrete wall until set hard; C,C, concrete foundation wall; B, anchor bolt; S, stone sub-base.

Fig. 12 shows section view of foundation wall with sill and concrete floor; G, ground level.

Fig. 13 shows cedar post set in concrete with a sub-base of stone. Pan on top of post is to keep rats from working thru floor. Sill as fitted at house corner is shown. G, G, ground level; C, C, concrete filled in around post and rounded off above ground level; S, stone base which helps to keep post dry; B, anchor bolt.

Building Materials

If I were to build again and could have my choice of materials, 1 should frame my poultry house with comparatively light material and enclose it with a single wall of red cedar matched or novelty siding only. Roof either of same material or of smooth boards covered with asbestos shingles. Heavy walled or double walled poultry houses are not necessary. I believe that a house of material named would cost less in the end, prove comfortable at all times and require but little time to build.

Usually in poultry house building one has to use such material as he can get cheaply, often second hand lumber.

Spruce makes excellent framing material, but whatever framing is available can be made to serve.

For sills on concrete foundation 2x4s are ample, on a post foundation use 4x4s or 4x6s. Studs 2x3s. Plates 2x3s. Rafters and floor timbers 2x4s as a rule. Small houses do well with a 2x3 rafter.

Houses where floor span is considerable and where heavy-weights use the house, 2x6s or 2x8s may make better floor timbers.

Where house is to be shingled or covered with roofing fabric any good covering-in boards will serve if fairly smooth on side that goes inside house. To avoid having mites accumulate between shingles and covering-in boards dip shingles in creosote shingle stain before laying. It can be had in three colors, brown, green and red.

Second quality shingles are good enough for side walls, but it does not pay to put anything but 1st extra clears on roofs.

Roofing fabric will last indefinitely if given a coat of asphaltum every year or two. If not so treated, there is no roofing that I have ever used that will last over ten years.

Window sashes can be bought ready made and glazed and should be painted before putting in. Window casings are usually cheaper to buy ready made to fit windows than to make. Door frames I have always made of white pine and doors of matched pine, door cleats put on with screws. So made and the door kept painted there will be very little if any swelling or warping.

There will be more about building materials and construction as we go into details of plans for several good types of fresh-air houses.

CHAPTER III

Plans and Instructions for Building Woods' Small Colony House, Portable *K-D Type—Frost in Poultry House

"We cannot be over-mindful of the facts that clear fresh air continuously, pure clean water for drink, and untainted food and quarters are highly promotive of the health of poultry, and at all seasons. But we are constrained again to affirm that of all these, pure air for them to breathe is of first and last importance towards their continuous health and thrift."—H. H. Stoddard, Poultry World, Sept. 1876.

TO AVOID possible misunderstandings and a great deal of inconvenience to all concerned, I wish to state here that I do not have any poultry house plans for sale, that I cannot supply blue prints, special plans, nor building instructions by mail. Such houses as I recommend will be described in detail and plans given, with information sufficiently complete to enable any reader, familiar with common carpenter work, to build. Any reader who has had no experience in building can take the plans and measurements given herein to his local carpenter, lumber merchant, or wooden box manufacturer and get any additional information which may be required at nominal cost.

From my own experience I would say that any boy in his 'teens, or man, who is at all familiar with the use of carpenter's tools and who studies illustrations and text, should be able to do a creditable job at building. In most cases the material to be used will have to be determined at the time and place of building. Economy in building depends to a large extent upon economy in buying and making best use of such material as is available locally. The available supply of building materials differs a great deal in different localities and at different times. Look over the offerings by local dealers and building wreckers. Often second-hand lumber is available at a low price. A number of years ago, when living within easy reach of railroad car shops, I bought old freight car doors at ten cents each and made excellent use of them in poultry house building by adapting my plans a little to this low cost material.

Much as I should enjoy correspondence with readers, I cannot undertake personal correspondence concerning house building and house plans.

Frost in Poultry House

As stated elsewhere the open-front house is a dry house and practically free from frost. But any house may, when weather conditions

(*Knock-Down).

are right, show some frost in cold weather or "sweat" when humidity is excessive.

One would think to listen to some critics—and "the anvil chorus" —that they had never noted dampness nor frost in well-built dwellings, barns, and particularly in closed poultry houses. When such "observers" begin to talk or write on the subject, I feel like saying, as does "little Jeff" of the joke cartoons, "For the love of Mike, Mutt, be reasonable."

Everyone knows that well-built dwellings show dampness and frost when weather conditions favor either. I live in a well-built, modernized, old fashioned house. It was erected about 200 years ago and much of the original building remains in fine condition. There have been few changes made, except to introduce modern conveniences, more and larger windows, a screened sleeping porch, etc. As I write this on an August "dog-day," with windows open and the sun warming things up outside after a chilly night, our old fashioned fireplaces in the big chimney are beaded with "sweat," the desk drawers stick, and there is other evidence of general humidity.

Such conditions are general in all dwelling houses under similar weather conditions. In summer the window glass steams up with the sudden advent of cooler temperatures or after a thunder shower. In winter, with the kettle, or boiler, steaming on the kitchen range, the windows fog with condensed moisture, and if there is freezing temperature outside, the frost forms in patterns on the glass. We take such things as a matter of course. If we consider them at all, we attribute them to natural causes, and we do not "throw a fit" and proclaim the dwelling unfit to live in.

On this same humid day that this is written, one of my 10x16 Woods' open-front houses, which now holds some 90 or more half grown chickens, and another house of same size occupied by 30 layers—both houses with fronts always open, windows open and doors most of the time—are sufficiently dry to be dusty. This in spite of the fact that we have had a long spell of wet weather with little sunshine and one of the houses was recently drenched with whitewash put on with a spray pump.

Use a little common-sense in regard to the poultry house. Frost or dampness is often excessive in a closed house, the air therein is stale and bad, and there may be thick frost on the windows when winter weather favors such conditions. The files of any poultry paper will be found well supplied with complaints about such dampness, frost and bad air, as far back as one may be able to follow them. It is an old, old story.

Conditions are much better in the open-front house. At times there may be a little frost or dampness due to weather conditions, but never an excess unless the house is crowded far beyond its capacity. The air is fresh and wholesome. Just remember that a house containing 50 fowls has 50 high temperatured individuals burning oxygen rapidly to keep their "boilers" going and that each is exhaling large quantities of moisture and carbonic acid with every breath. This moisture and "bad air" must go somewhere. If it does not all escape thru the open front some of the moisture is bound to condense as water droplets—"sweat"—or frost on the cold windows and boards. The more fowls in the house, the more moisture and "bad air" to be gotten rid of. In many years' experience and in different localities, with a wide range of climate, I have never found dampness or frost

Part of chicken range with outdoor brooders. The Anchorage Farm, owned by Dr. Woods, Silver Lake, Mass. Woods' house, 10x16, is shown in background. Larger building is feed house and incubator cellar. As evidence of soil fertility produced by chickens, this range is in corn, beans, and potatoes, with some pole beans in one corner, mammoth Russian sun-flowers used for bean poles, some of latter over 12 ft. tall.

troublesome in open-front houses, even in heavy foggy weather. The reverse has usually been the case, the interior of the house being dry and often rather dusty. If this dust did not escape thru the open front it might prove a nuisance.

Some users of open-front houses have double glazed their window sash, that is put glass on inside of sash as well as the outside to form an air space between, and claim that this prevents frost forming on the windows. I do not consider it worth while to go to the extra expense of double glazing the sash; there is bother enough keeping ordinary windows in good order with putty, glass and paint.

A good many poultry houses have been built with double walls and a dead air space between. Here in the New England climate—

and probably in locations where winter is even more severe—I believe that this is an unnecessary extra expense. Most of my houses have been single board wall covered with shingles, but two, which have been in constant use, are very simply built with a single wall of matched boards, painted. One was built of boards which were not sufficiently seasoned and cracks have opened between some of the boards. These cracks have been left "as is," no battens considered necessary. All of these houses are open-fronts and some have been used for brood sows and their litters in late winter and early spring, when not needed for fowls. A poultry house is more sightly without cracks in the walls, so it is a good plan to use dry well-seasoned lumber for building and to keep the houses painted. The cracks are mentioned here for the benefit of timid people who may fear fresh air for poul-

Fig. 14—Experimental Woods' Open-Front House built in 1908. View of west side.

try. I have not had any trouble whatever in keeping fowls healthy in such houses, these fresh-air flocks all have the habit of health and seem immune to colds and diseases.

Like lots of other "troubles" many "poultry troubles" may be more the result of imagination on the part of the poultry keeper than actual happenings, while in other instances an unobserving poultryman may not know his birds are sick until they begin to die. It is a good plan to study and observe the flocks closely, but don't coddle them or fret and worry. I have seen quite a number of poultry keepers fretting and worrying about their flocks when the birds were perfectly normal and doing well. On the other hand, a well-informed and observing poultryman will note indications which would escape the ordinary observer and ward off any real trouble before it gets a foothold in the flock.

Woods' House, Portable K-D Type

.. Several sets of plans for building Woods' fresh-air poultry houses will be given in the chapters to come, showing up-to-date improvements which are the result of experience and observation, covering fifteen years of practical work with this type of house, under widely different conditions.

The first Woods' open-front house was built for experimental purposes, under my direction, on the farm of John W. Dwinell, Topsfield, Mass., in 1908. Fig. 14 shows west side and front of this house. This house, having floor dimensions 8x14 ft., being located close to other farm buildings, was set on posts with inverted pans between posts and sills to make building rat-proof. It has a double board floor. Fowls kept in this house have given entirely satisfactory results and have enjoyed the best of health. The house is still in use. Detail plan is not given here as dimensions of similar type of house, which follows, are preferred.

Side Elevation and Ground Plan

Figure 15 shows side elevation, sectional view, of Woods' open-front poultry house, portable knock-down type. Below in same illustration is shown the floor or ground plan. The dimensions of this building are 10 ft. wide, 16 ft. from front to rear, 4 ft. 4 inches high in front, 8 ft. 3 inches high at top of monitor, 4 ft. 7 inches high in rear. Height includes distance from bottom of sill to top of roof board.

The illustration shows location of nests, water pail, roosts, dropping board, windows, door and screens. I usually provide four nests in location shown for flock of 15 to 20 fowls; for larger flocks up to 40, I use double bank of nests in same position.

It is a good plan to provide an inside screen of one-inch mesh hexagon wire on a wooden frame, hinged at the top to swing in, for each window in monitor top. The monitor-top window is hinged at the top to swing outward. A screen door of same size wire netting, made to swing in as shown in ground plan, is a great convenience. I usually run these houses with monitor-top windows open from April until late fall. The door is kept open thru the day in hot weather, also the side windows. One side window, on lee side, is kept open day and night in warm weather. It makes a very comfortable house summer and winter.

In winter the windows and door are kept closed, except on warm sunny days when the monitor-top windows are opened for two or three hours during the warmest part of the day.

The compass in ground plan shows how house should front in New England location to get best advantage of sun both summer and winter. Note course of sun in your location and place house so that it will get sun thru front and windows for as long a period as possible in the short days of winter.

As shown in the plans, this house is built in sections. It will be a good plan to map it out on the floor of barn or shed, where parts can be held in place by cleats until boards are brought as close together as possible and fastened in position. Use well-seasoned dry lumber, cement-coated wire nails; screws, bolts and other hardware to fit.

If you are not accustomed to building knock-down houses, any carpenter or wooden box manufacturer should be able to make up sections of house at reasonable cost.

The Side Sections

Fig. 16 shows construction of side sections, inside view with detail of frame—shaded parts—windows, door and boarding. These sections are built of planed matched boards with 2x3 in. stuff for framing. "A" is west wall of rear part of house, "B" is east wall of same part. Both "A" and "B" are 10 ft. long at base, 4 ft. 6 in. high at rear and 8 ft. 2 in. high in front. This gives a top line, to support roof, 10 ft. 8 in. long. The 2x3 framing is flush with outside of section all around, top plate and the bottom sill being full length. In "A" the middle brace 2x3 runs the whole length of section between end studs, it serves as a support for roosts in both "A" and "B", the brace is 2 ft. 9 in. from bottom of sill to top of brace. Cleats are shown in "A" on top of this brace to hold roosts in place; same are used in "B" also but not indicated on plan. The short 2x3 below brace is support for droppings board, 1 ft. from bottom of brace to top of this support. In "B" a third stud 6 ft. 6 in. long is used for rear side of door frame, other 2x3s used as indicated to complete a door frame 2 ft. 7 in. wide by 5 ft. high. The boarding on outside of this section "B" does not come within one inch of inside edges of this door frame leaving space for door to overlap frame and break joints.

Section "C" is west wall of front of house, "D" is east wall, both inside views to show framing, same dimensions apply to each. Base and sill are 6 ft. long, top and plate are 6 ft. 2 in. long; back of section, which attaches to rear section, is 5 ft. 6 in. high; front is 4 ft. 3 in. The frame strips which run from back to front are to frame window and are placed at right distance apart to take a half sash, with 6 lights. In outside boarding the hole for window is made one inch smaller than sash all around. The window is shown in place in "D", this window illustrated is 2 ft. 6¾ in. wide by 2 ft. 2 in. high. Cleats fastened to frame to make window runway or slide are shown in "D". Bottom of window—top of lower 2x3 used as window frame—is 18 in. from bottom of sill. Rear side of window hole in "C" is 14 in. from outside of stud.

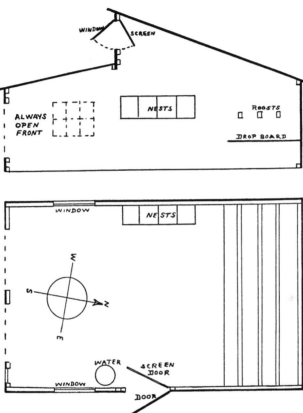

Fig. 15—Sectional view side elevation (upper), ground or floor plan (lower). Woods' Open-Front House, 10x16, portable K-D type, 40 fowls or less. Position of windows, doors, screens and furnishings indicated.

Before boarding in frame, drill studs, in rear of front section and front of rear section, to match and take bolts which hold these sections together. Bolts to parallel long way of house. Three bolts required for each side, top and bottom bolts within 1 ft. of top and bottom of front section, third bolt midway between. "C" bolts to "A" and "D" to "B" sills flush at bottom. 2x3 framing stuff seldom runs true to measure; be sure to measure and fit all parts. Keep bottom corners, where stud joins sill, clean right angles—use a steel square.

Monitor-Top and Front Sections

Fig. 17 shows the monitor-top or top window section open-wire-front section, detail sectional view of the monitor-top window, including position of plate for front roof—do not overlook this. Also detail of front and rear rafters which run thru middle of house and support roof sections. The rear rafter is 10 ft. 8 in. long and fits into notches in top plate of monitor and plate of rear wall. The front rafter is 6 ft. 2 in. long, notched to fit front roof plate at base of monitor top, front side, and notch in middle of plate of open-wire-front section. In my own house these middle rafters are 2x3 stuff but on account of weight of winter snow on rear roof I have found it desirable to support it near center—in front of dropping board—with a 2x3 stud from floor to rafter. This prevents roof from sagging in middle.

The monitor or top window section is 10 ft. wide by 2 ft. 11 in. high, overall. The view is from inside to show frame, except front roof plate which is shown in detail of top window. The plates run to within about 3 inches of the edge of boarding at both sides. The exact width of this overlap of boards beyond frame will depend upon the width of matched boards and the stud and plate of side sections "A" and "B" at this point as this top section screws on to upper part of studs of front of "A" and "B" to make a flush joint at outside. Base of this top section carries a notch at each side, below rear base plate, which fits inside sides, so that height of overlap is 2 ft. 8 in. as shown in illustration. This is distance from bottom of inside or rear base plate to top of upper plate. The studs at ends and in center are 2 ft. 2 in. high, the distance between top of rear base plate and upper plate. The front roof plate is on front side of the monitor-top section flush with boarding at base. It is notched in center to receive end of middle rafter for front roof. The short 2x3s between studs form the window sills and tops of these are just 10 inches from bottom of rear base plate. The top of the upper plate is 22 in. from top of window sills. The boarding is put on up and down on this frame at ends and in center. The board in center is 8 in. wide. At top and bottom between these upright boards the boarding is horizontal, a top board 4 in. wide and two base or bottom boards, the upper one 8 in. and the lower 5 in. wide. This should leave openings both sides of center to take a three light cellar window 3 ft. 8 in. wide by 18 inches. These top windows are hinged at the top to swing out toward front. To each, at sides and bottom on outsides are nailed thin battens to overlap about one inch to keep out weather. A window rod of strap iron about 22 in. long, bored with holes large enough to admit head of wire nail, is attached to middle of sash near bottom by a staple or screw eye. A convenient nail in middle of window sill serves as a stop to fasten window rod, so that window can be opened at any angle desired.

The open wire front section is 10 ft. wide by 4 ft. 3 in. high. There are two sills at base and two plates at top, separated by small 3 in. stud blocks and a center stud 2 ft. 8 in. long. Upper plate notched in center for rafter. The boarding overlaps frame about 3 in., or sufficient to allow a flush tight joint with side walls when attached to same by screws. This overlap if one inch boards are used should be three inches; if ⅞ in. boards, 2⅞ in.; if ⅝ in. boards, 2⅝ in.;—provided always that the studding in frame is exactly 2 inches. Stock varies, measure your stock and make sections fit tight and flush at corner joints.

This open-front section is boarded up and down at ends and center. Cover in about 1½ ft. from each end and use 8 in. board in center. Use horizontal board 9 in. wide at top and 10 in. board at bottom be-

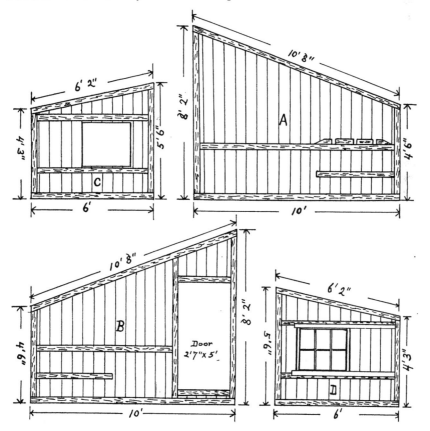

Fig. 16—Construction plans of side sections Woods' Open-Front House, 10x16, portable K-D type. Shaded parts show frame. See text.

tween the upright boarding. This should leave openings both sides of center 3 ft. 2 in. wide by 2 ft. 8 in. high. Protect this opening with one quarter inch square mesh wire netting—or "wire cloth"—such as is used for protecting cellar windows. Put on with strong staples. "D" is opening for fowls, to be closed by a slide.

Rear Wall and Roof Sections

Fig. 18 shows rear wall, roof sections, door and detail of corner. All except corner detail, which is a sectional view looking down, are interior views.

Rear wall has sill and plate of 2x3 stuff—shaded in illustration—flush at top and bottom of section. Plate notched in center for rear rafter. Boarding overlaps frame, in same manner as described in top and front sections, to permit screwing to the side section studs to make close flush joint. As shown this overlap is about three inches—see description in previous section.

Rear roof is made in two sections, as one piece would be too heavy to handle. Both east and west sides of roof are shown in plan (Fig. 18). The shaded frame here is not made of heavy stock but is planed finished stock about ⅞ in. stuff. The front frame strip is about 5 in. wide, rear about 4 in. wide, both flush with edge of section. Outside strip is 3 inches wide. Inside strip (middle of roof) is 3 in. wide and one inch from edge, to permit boards to overlap on middle rafter. Midway between front and back is a cleat of board 8 inches wide put on with screws to brace roof and prevent warping. The board cleat and the inside frame strip, at both ends, are about 3 in. from edge of frame strip. This permits the roof when in place to fit down snug over ends and sides. It is fastened in place with screws at sides and middle. Each rear roof section is 5 ft. 3 in. by 11 ft. 7 in.

The two front roof sections are made in same manner, except that there is no rear frame strip and front strip is 4 in. wide. East and west sections of roof are shown in plan (Fig. 18). Each front roof section is 5 ft. 3 in. by 6 ft. 7 in. Roof is fastened in place in same manner as rear roof. Roof sections are made of matched boards laid horizontally.

The door, 2 ft. 9 in. wide by 5 ft. 2 in. high, is shown in Fig. 18, indicating position of cleats and brace. Horizontal cleats are 6 in. wide, diagonal or brace cleat is 5 in. Use screws to put on cleats and brace. This door is hinged at right side as shown in ground plan.

The corner detail in Fig. 18 shows how sills (also plates) fit snug, and overlap of end sections fits on to side sections. Finish boards of 3 and 4 in. stock are shown on outside of corner to "break joints." This

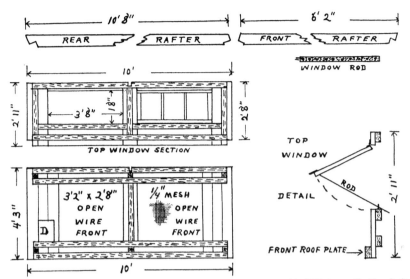

Fig. 17—Construction plans, Woods' Open-Front House, 10x16, portable K-D type. Sectional view of middle rafters above, also window rod. Top window section for monitor-top, open-wire-front section. Interior view, shaded parts show frame. Detail of top window and plates of top section, at right. See text.

makes a snug firm corner. Put on with screws if house is to be taken down.

Assembling House

If parts are properly made and fitted, two men or a man and boy can put this house together with very little trouble. Prepare a foundation of plank or 2x4s to keep sills off ground. If a floor is to be used it will be well to put this foundation on posts, stone or wood blocks, to keep house high enough so that dog can be put under it to get rid of rats. Lay floor before putting on roof.

Bolt together side sections "A" and "C", also "B" and "D." Raise these to upright position on foundation and brace in position with poles or braces of 2x3 stuff, from ground to top; hold brace at top with nail to prevent slipping. Then put rear wall in place and screw it to studs of sides. Put on open-wire-front in same manner. Follow this with monitor or top window piece. Be sure to have these sections fit snug and flush. Now put in the middle rafters and fasten with screws. The front roof should now go on and be screwed in place. Take away braces used to support sides first erected. Put on the big rear roof sections last. Make all roof sections fit snug around sides and in middle on rafter. If no floor is to be used, the 2x3 stud to support middle rafter in rear part of house can be put in position. If a floor is used, put this stud in after floor is laid.

Roofing fabric is used to cover both roofs. This should be put on up and down with generous laps, the middle piece being put on last to overlap on both sections of roof. In case house is to be taken down, it is only necessary to cut the middle piece of roofing. The boards of monitor top should be covered with roofing which should overlap roofing on front roof, to make tight joint below monitor or top window section. If desired, use roofing fabric on outside of rear wall.

Floor in Three Sections

Floor, if there is one, goes in before roof goes on. A wood floor of matched boards, built in three sections on top of 2x3 stringers, 2 in. side up, placed about 1½ ft. apart, is a great convenience for use with this house. The floor is made in sections and then laid. The 2x3 stringers should run across house from side to side to rest on 2x3 sills which form base of side walls. The matched boards are nailed to stringers at right angles so that they run from front to back of house. Use care in fitting floor so that edges of sections fit each other and whole floor fits snugly to sides of house all around. "Toe-nail" the floor sections at corners to the sills; that is drive nail in diagonally to fasten floor to sill close to wall, but leave the head of nail so that it can be grasped and pulled with a nail-puller or claw hammer, so that floor can be taken up easily.

Dropping board can be made in similar manner to floor section, using lighter material and light stringers of 1x2 in. stuff, 1 inch side next boards. Have stringers rest on 2x3 supports provided on side walls, see Fig. 16.

Windows, screen window, door, screen door, should now be put in place and a "safety-hasp" and padlock provided for the door. Hinge outside door on right hand side—toward the rear—to swing out, see ground plan, Fig. 15.

Either provide the side windows with a framed screen or put on one-inch mesh hexagon netting with staples on outside.

Use corner boards for finish of corners as shown in corner detail, Fig. 18. Use a 3 in. wide finish board on outside of sides and ends close up to roof all around house. Use a 3 in. finish board to cover joint of side sections.

Give the whole house two coats of good paint and keep it painted.

This portable K-D house makes a good building for renters as it can be taken down and shipped at moving time. It is convenient for use on every farm and it is not expensive to build, service and general usefulness considered.

It can be moved about the farm without taking it apart. I have one that was built for me by the E. C. Young Co., Randolph, Mass., along similar lines, that has been moved all around on my farm. We

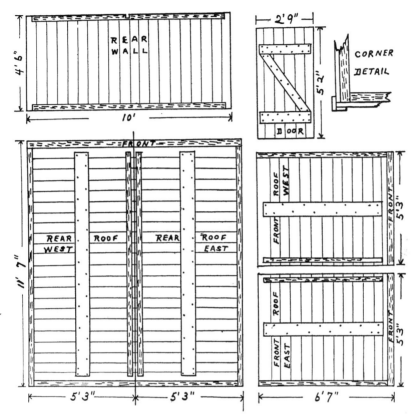

Fig. 18—Construction plans for rear wall, two sections of rear roof, two sections of front roof, and door; all interior views to show frame and braces. Also detail of corner finish. See text.

jacked it up, put long oak poles under it for skids and yanked it to where we wanted it with a pair of horses. It did not hurt the house any, but a better way would be to move it on rollers, or get some wheels under it.

A number of years ago I gave Mr. Young, of the above named company, permission to build portable Woods' open-front poultry houses, knock-down type, somewhat similar to the improved type described herein. He made a considerable number of Woods' houses for well-known poultry plants where quality fowls are grown, among them Owen Farms, Vineyard Haven, Mass., owned by Maurice F. Delano. After using these houses several years, Mr. Delano wrote me under date of June 29, 1922—"The Woods' house has been absolutely satisfactory from every angle. I wish I had several more up at the farm and eventually will have to have."

Altho the Young Company is the only portable house manufacturer I have authorized to build Woods' houses from my plans, I do not receive any remuneration or royalty on same and cannot undertake correspondence with readers concerning houses manufactured by this or any other concern. The improved plans here given should be sufficiently complete and directions plain enough to enable a novice to build successfully.

Where a number of these portable K-D houses are to be built it may be advisable to build them "rights and lefts;" that is some with doors in east side as shown in plans and others with doors in west side. It is an easy matter to change the plans "A" and "B" to provide for door in "A" instead of "B."

With such colony houses built "rights and lefts," they should be arranged in field with west doors opposite east doors, making it possible to enter two houses at one stop of cart or truck.

There will be more about Woods' houses, both colony and long or "continuous" types, also other fresh-air houses in the chapters to come.

CHAPTER IV

Plans and Instructions for Building the Howard Fresh-Air House and the Martin Colony House

*"Lucky indeed is the man, knowing little of the real ins and outs of poultry keeping, who starts in on the colony house, free range plan. **This man has at least a chance of staying in the business.**"*
—W. Theo. Wittman.

IN BULLETIN No. 219 of the Pennsylvania Department of Agriculture, W. Theo. Wittman, one of the experts of the department, says concerning open-front poultry houses:

"The old theory that hens to lay well in winter had to have a warm, tight house was no good in that it would only work occasionally. The new theory that the house was to be flooded with fresh, cold, pure air all the time and at the same time be a good shelter brings about conditions whereby it is possible to have a good winter egg yield every season.

"This use of cold, fresh air brought about by the adoption of the open-front house has brought many poultry people to the point where they no longer fear or even look for that old-time dreadful winter scourge of poultry, the roup. One of the finest things about this use of open-front houses is that the wonderful stimulating and health giving properties of the abundance of fresh air supplied are cumulative and the poultry takes on new life and is in effect, in a few generations, really a different kind of poultry. Poultry that has been kept for successive generations in a good open-front house and otherwise well cared for rarely is sick. The eggs hatch, the chicks live, in short poultry keeping with most of the ills omitted is made possible.

"A few poultrymen will go even a little further and claim trap nest records showing that in open-front houses they can get more eggs out of a certain number of hens of the American class in cold weather than at any one other season of the year.

"We have used a wide open and a curtain front house and variations of the same for many years and we know whereof we speak, when we advocate no other style of house but an open-front one . After finding how beautifully it worked we went pretty near the limit and we feel sure today that under certain circumstances in the climate of southern Pennsylvania, the limit can be safely gone and a house can be not only 'open-front' but it can have cracks and holes elsewhere. * * * * *

"To many even yet this seems a most radical, even revolutionary, departure from all accepted ideas and theories as to poultry housing. We have found many people who have argued with us that the idea was not a good one or a sound one, or even a safe one, (having in mind frozen combs, frozen eggs and the probability of no eggs at all in winter) but we have never yet found a single individual who has tried it who has not spoken highly of it."

The same authority writing about how to get "bumper winter egg yields," after calling attention to the importance of having pullets uniformly matured and ready to lay early in October, getting them into winter quarters in good season, giving a well-balanced ration and heavy feeding, says:

"A wide-open-front for the house is the next thing to be looked to. Or, roosting that has as much ventilation as all out-doors and yet is perfectly sheltered from drafts and weather. It is proposed that these pullets roost thus all winter and it is highly important that this is begun in early fall. There will thus be no frosted combs and there will be a great many more eggs than in a tight or 'warm' house."

Lest some reader say that the above, while it may apply to southern Pennsylvania, may not prove true where the winters are more severe, I want to say that the open-front house has given an equally good account of itself in the northern and central uplands of the state, also in eastern and northern New York where the winters are very cold and the snowfall heavy.

In an interview given in 1910, Prof. W. R. Graham, Ontario Agricultural College, Guelph, Canada, said: "To date the single-boarded, open-front house has proved superior for getting eggs in winter and keeping the fowls in a healthy state."

The 1909 report of the Department of Agriculture for the Province of British Columbia contains the following:

"In place of the curtain-front houses we find the open-front houses giving better satisfaction. Considering the climatic conditions of this Province, the open-front house is deemed most advisable.

"What the curtain front house was to the closed house, that the modern fresh-air house is to the curtain-front house. The advantages of this house over the curtain-front house are many. It is less expensive and less labor is required in tending the flocks. A larger supply of pure air is supplied to the fowls at all times, thus keeping the birds in better health, with an increase in the fertility of the eggs and a larger egg yield.

"The birds are protected at all times from drafts by the tight back, sides and roof. Only one side of the house being open, cold winds do not penetrate the house. The fowls are more comfortable all of the time and seem to enjoy the greater abundance of fresh air than is supplied by the old closed house or when the air is diffused thru a curtain.

"In brief, a cheaply built house with an open front, will give equally as good results, if not better, than a more expensive or warmer house. Not only will poultry lay more eggs if the house is supplied with plenty of fresh air, but the hatchability of the eggs from such houses will be greater, and a stronger and more thrifty brood of chickens will be the result."

Fig. 19—The Howard Fresh-Air House as originally built, front and east end. The curtain has been discarded for a number of years, that portion of front being always open. The large window shown in east end has been displaced by a door and small window duplicating the west end.

From letters received from poultrymen all over the American continent and from many foreign lands, including hot, temperate and cold climates, the open-front poultry house has given satisfaction wherever it has been given an honest trial, and after many years of practical use it continues to give satisfaction. Now and then some poultryman, located in a section where there are many others who are getting fine results with open-front houses, seems unable to get equally satisfactory results. If the open-front house is built as recommended and if it is properly located as to air drainage and land drainage, it should be obvious that the type of house is not at fault.

The trouble may be with the man, the food or the method of feeding, or possibly with the stock itself. The stock, however, is seldom at fault if properly bred, given common sense care during the growing stage and properly and well fed. Of course no reasonable person would expect to get good results with stock that was coddled and babied all thru the growing period, kept in close or crowded coops, and fed a poorly balanced ration. To get maximum benefits from fresh-air or open-front housing, fowls should have had the benefit of fresh-air methods combined with good care and good feeding from the shell to the laying house—and preferably should be out of fresh-air breeding stock bred for health. But it is possible to get very much better results with any average flock by keeping them in open-front houses and feeding well. While it is preferable to have birds in their open-front quarters before cold weather sets in, I have repeatedly taken fowls from closed houses, from training and exhibition coops, and from snug, stuffy shipping coops which had been for days in over-heated express cars, and transferred them to open-front houses at all seasons without any ill results, tho occasionally a male bird with large comb, in spite of having comb rubbed with petrolatum, has experienced slight frostbite—he would have had comb frostbitten just the same in a closed house and it might have been more severe.

All flocks should be fed heavily in winter, particularly so if a big egg yield is expected. At all times in winter they need plenty of heat and fat forming foods well balanced with proteins and with greens and raw vegetables. They need an ample supply of feather and shell forming foods—mineral foods such as are found in oyster shells and good granite grits—not only for the food value of the minerals but to insure proper functioning of all parts of the body. This is very necessary for some time prior to and during the fall molt. Modern open-front houses are very nearly "fool proof," but no flock, however well it may be housed, is proof against the errors of a keeper who does not know how to feed. The man behind the feed pail has a big responsibility for the ultimate results and he must know his business.

Young stock reared under fresh-air methods and adult fowls kept in open-front houses tend to carry brighter and heavier plumage than flocks that get less open-air living. The feathers are longer and of fine texture, the fluff and the under-plumage are heavier and more abundant; even with "loose feathered" Asiatics the general effect is of closer feathering. The body is broader and deeper. The whole appearance of the bird indicates health, vigor and vitality.

The Howard Fresh-Air House

On a rather abrupt hillside overlooking the head of Buzzards Bay, Mass., is located the "Head of the Bay Poultry Farm" owned by Walter Scott Howard, who before he retired from the stage, was a member of our beloved Joseph Jefferson's company of players.

The farm carries Barred Plymouth Rocks exclusively, catering to a private trade in fancy fresh brown eggs and, in season, supplying incubator eggs for hatcheries. This is one of the well known successful practical poultry plants in the heart of Massachusetts' shore vacation land. To make a success of such a business the stock must be in the pink of condition and enjoy the best of health. All of the flocks are housed in open-front "fresh-air" colony houses to make this certain.

From the bay and from the shore drive the visitor sees a number of attractive colony houses and large yards, well placed on the side hill. All are Howard fresh-air houses. The location is one where high winds sweep over it frequently and all houses are anchored to their foundations.

When the first buildings were erected, a considerable number of years ago, the original houses of the Howard type had curtain fronts and large east windows. The curtains were discarded as unnecessary long ago. For greater convenience the large east window has been displaced by a smaller window and a door, making the east end a duplicate of the west end. Fig. 19 shows the house as originally built.

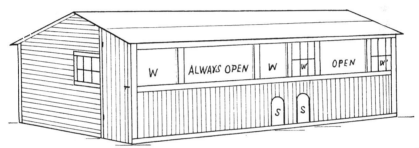

Fig. 20—Front and West end of Howard Fresh-Air House as now used and successfully operated for a number of years at "Head of Bay Poultry Farm," Buzzards Bay, Mass. "W.W" front windows removed for summer. "W,W'" front windows as used in winter. End windows are hinged at top and open in. Door opens out. Ends are boarded horizontally. Front, back and roof are boarded up and down. All matched boards. Roof covered with roofing fabric. Windows and open front protected by one-inch-mesh hexagon poultry wire. "S,S" slides or poultry doors.

Fig. 20 shows front and west end elevation of the Howard fresh-air house as in use today and for several years past. "W,W" are spaces for winter windows on either side of the always-open-front. "W',W' " shows the windows in place as used in winter. These front windows are kept out all of the time from the first mild days of early spring until settled cold weather and snow come in late fall. The end window is hinged at the top to open up and hook to roof boards. It is kept open most of the time in spring, summer and fall. The door is hinged to open out as indicated. The window and door in east end are directly opposite those in west end. Door in west end gives access to walk and driveway, door in east end opens into the yard. "S,S" are slides giving fowls access to yard.

This house is built on a concrete foundation. The sills, studs and rafters are all 2x4 stock. The dimensions are 10 ft. wide by 20 ft. long inside of sills, which gives an over-all ground dimension of 10 ft.

8 in. by 20 ft. 8 in. The front and rear studs (or corner posts) are 5 ft. 6 in. high from top of sill. The roof has a double pitch which is rather flat, the height of building from top of sill to top of middle rafter is 7 ft.

The method of framing this house is somewhat unusual but is strong and economical of frame material. Fig. 21 shows detail of frame of front and west end, also front roof. Balance of house duplicates this frame plan. "W" indicates windows. "O" the open front. "D" the door. It will be noted that besides the two front studs which are also corner posts, each 5 ft. 6 in. high, there is only one other long stud which comes in center and reaches from sill to plate. The ends of plate, which is also the outer rafter, are butted to the tops of

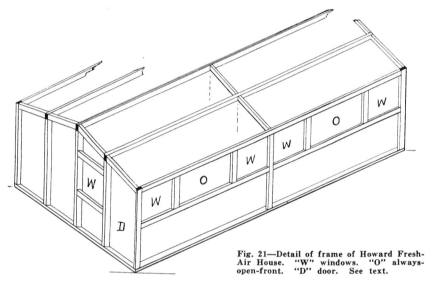

Fig. 21—Detail of frame of Howard Fresh-Air House. "W" windows. "O" always-open-front. "D" door. See text.

corner posts making a flush joint, top of post is shown in black in plan. The long stringers from corner posts to center stud are 3 ft. from top of sill to top of stringer. From top of stringer to bottom of plate there are, on each side of center stud, two short studs each 2 ft. 2 in. high. These are spaced about 2 ft. 6 in. from corner posts and center posts as shown, or spaced to take the available half sash windows. When house is boarded in these windows are approximately 2 ft. 4 in. wide by 2 ft. high in the clear, but each house builder should measure the half sash windows available for his use and make the opening to fit. "O" is space for always-open-front between the winter windows. In plan this space is 4 ft. wide. The short studs shown in front are not used for rear wall, the corner posts and center stud

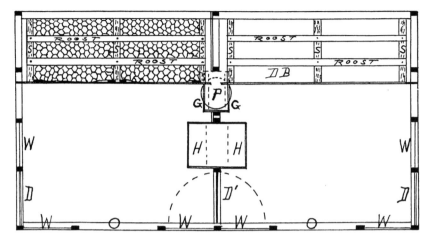

Fig. 22—Ground Plan Howard Fresh-Air House. Left pen shows detail of wire floor to roost supports (S). Right pen shows roosts and supports with wire removed exposing slanting dropping board which forms hopper for collecting droppings. Grit hopper (G) and mash hopper (H) are built in middle partition. "P" is water pan below grit hopper. "W" window. "D,D" doors. "D'" door in partition. "O" always open front. See text.

being sufficient. As shown in plan the rafters are horizontal, one at middle or peak of roof and one on each side of same midway between it and plate or outside rafter. Rafters beveled to make roof boards lay snug.

End studding is placed to permit a doorway at "D" 2 ft. 6 in. from stud to stud. Short stringers between door stud and middle stud are placed to fit a half sash window. Door and window in east end are placed next front in same manner, door opening out just opposite. Short braces are used between rafters at top of studs at both ends of building and in center. There is also a center sill which supports partition midway between ends dividing house into two pens. This sill is indicated in ground plan, Fig. 22, but is not shown in frame plan.

As shown in elevation, Fig. 20, the ends of the house are boarded horizontally, except door which is up and down and the 3 in. finish strips at corners and at side of door and window. Front and back are boarded up and down. Front has finish boards at top and bottom and around openings, as indicated. Roof is boarded up and down, with sufficient overhang allowed at ends and at eaves in front and rear. Overhang at eaves is about 6 inches. The roof boards are covered with a good roofing fabric. All boarding is of sound, clear, dry matched stock and outside of house is kept well painted. Interior is whitewashed as often as may be necessary to keep it bright and sweet. Openings for windows and the always-open-front are covered with one-inch mesh hexagon poultry netting.

The ground plan, Fig. 22, should be studied together with end-section view, Fig. 23, which shows partition and the house furnishings. In Fig. 22 the 2x4 sills which are anchored by bolts to concrete foundation are outlined and position of studs or posts indicated in solid black. "W" indicates windows, "D" outer doors, "D'" door in partition, hinged at outside to swing both ways. "O" the always-open-front. "G" is grit and shell hopper. "H" is dry mash hopper. "P" is water pan below grit hopper. The two hoppers and the shelf for water pan are built into the partition to supply both pens.

The roosts and dropping boards or rather dropping hopper "DB" are unusual in design. See Fig. 23 in which roosts are indicated in black marked "R". The roost support "R-S" is made up of three 2x4 strips hinged by rear ends to rear wall stringer. These roost supports—"S" in ground plan—are joined in front by a long 1x2 cleat which forms a frame. To this frame is fastened 2-inch-mesh hexagon poultry netting to make a floor for roost supports and to form a cover for droppings hopper ("DB"). This wire netting is indicated in left pen in ground plan.

The dropping board is made of matched stock laid horizontally on two end and one or two middle cleats of boards 4 to 6 in. wide. These cleats are flush with bottom of dropping board but extend about 2 in. beyond top, here they engage the cleat on roost supports which drops over them to lock dropping board in position. Lift up roost support and dropping board is released. The dropping board extends from rear sill to roost supports as shown in Fig. 23, fitting snugly to end wall and partition to form a hopper to collect droppings. The dropping board is not made fast and lifts out for cleaning. With a flock of healthy fowl this dropping hopper can go all winter without need of cleaning out, which saves labor over ordinary dropping boards which must be cleaned daily. The roosts "R,R" are not made fast to the roost supports. They are drilled at ends and in center to fit on spikes which project from roost supports and can be easily lifted off when desired. Kept clean and kerosened now and then, they are practically mite proof. The dropping hopper does not collect mites, as would accumulations of droppings close beneath roosts. Mr. Howard assures me that he seldom sees any mites and has never found them below the roost supports. The dropping board is kept bright with whitewash and the space immediately in front of it makes a favorite place for the fowls' dust bath.

As indicated in Fig. 23, the partition is mostly of matched boards. A small portion in front of peak of roof is of wire. Upper part of partition door is of wire netting, lower part is wire netting covered with burlap—to keep males from scrapping. The mash hopper is built between the partition studs as if it were one big hopper—which it is—provided with feeding tray in each pen. Grit hopper is a smaller edition of the mash hopper. The water pan rests on a shelf just above the sill and below the grit hopper. "N" is battery of nests built of light smooth crate material and wire netting. There are six nests and they hang in hangers of lath or crate material from the rafters much as the ordinary cellar shelf is swung from floor timbers. Each battery of nests is built on a frame of crate material and one-inch-mesh wire netting, the nest shelf "NS," which rests on the supports fastened to rafters and is held in place by end cleats. "ND" is door to nests made of wire netting and crate material and hinged to rafter or the supports. The nests have wire netting bottoms, are light in weight and easily removable for cleaning. End next the partition is close up. Access to nests is from opposite end, an easy jump from roosts. When pullets first occupy the house this open end is temporarily closed by a wire door, just at roosting time, to prevent pullets from roosting in nests. Adult fowls have not given any trouble thru attempting to roost in nests. The bottom of nest frame is about 7 ft. long by 2 ft. 6 in. wide, which allows for nests 14 in. from front to back and either six large or eight medium nests spaced equally with a nest shelf, for fowls to alight on, 16 in. by 7 ft. The support

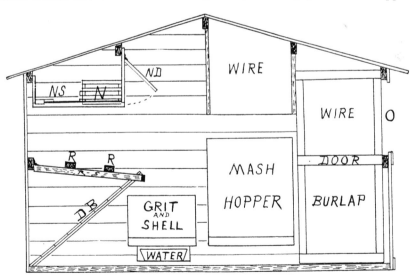

Fig. 23—Section View Howard Fresh-Air House showing furnishings and partition between pens. Partition is largely matched boards except where indicated otherwise. "DB" slanting dropping board forming hopper. "R,R" roosts. "R.S" roost support, black end shows end cleat which locks over upright cleats of dropping board. "N" nests. "NS" nest shelf "ND" nest door. "O" open front. See text.

for the nest shelf is about 20 inches above the roost support at rear of house.

Roost supports are about 2 ft. 6 in. above top of sill. Dropping board is about 4 ft..3 in. wide, including overlap of cleats, and full width of pen. Outer edge of roost support cleat is about 3 ft. 6 in. from rear wall.

To some these nests up near the roof will seem over-high for fowls as heavy as Plymouth Rocks, but actual experience will convince the doubters that the nests are alright. Mr. Howard's birds do not make any difficulty of it and seem to prefer the high nests. Nests are bedded with straw and are easy to keep clean.

The Howard fresh-air house is thoroly practical, has been in use long enough to prove its worth. With all windows open it is a cool house in summer and with windows in place and the always-open-front protected only by one-inch-mesh wire netting it is a comfortable house in winter. Even in blizzards very little snow drifts into the open front.

This house can be readily adapted for a long continuous house if desired, simply extending the house to desired length with partitions every 10 feet.

Each pen will accommodate 25 layers, or 50 fowls to the house. In localities where heavy snows are common in winter, I would prefer to have roof less flat—make roof about 1 foot higher at peak.

The slides or poultry doors in front of Howard fresh-air house are operated by window cord passing thru pulleys and ending at side of west door. Each slide has a cord attached to top which passes thru a galvanized iron pulley fastened to roof plate directly above slide. Beyond the pulleys both cords are joined to a single cord which passes thru a pulley midway along plate and another at top of corner post and from there to a cleat on corner post at convenient height just inside the door. The slides work easily and can be opened or closed by the attendant without entering the house.

The Martin Colony House

Now let us shift the scene to a colder climate and from practical or utility flocks to show birds that "have stood the test." John S. Martin, of Port Dover, Ontario, Canada, is widely known as the breeder of Regal Dorcas White Wyandottes, fowl that combine beauty with high egg production.

The Martin colony house is extensively used on his plant. It is an inexpensive open-front house, the opening being partly closed by a curtain, built on a frame, during severe storms in winter. Usually the curtain is hooked up against the rafters out of the way. If the house was built considerably deeper, no curtain would be necessary.

Fig. 24 shows a photographic view of the south front and east end of the Martin colony house after a snow storm in early winter. This house is 8 ft. deep by 12 ft. wide. It is 7 ft. stud in front and 5 ft. 6 in. stud at back. The front openings are each 3 ft. high by 4 ft. 6 in. wide. There is a 4-light window in each end and a door in east end.

Sills are 4x4 stock, corner studs and rafters 2x4s, balance of frame 2x3s. Fig. 25, left lower plan shows how front frame is built, right lower plan shows frame for east end, space 2 ft. 6 in. by 6 ft. is left between studs for door. This house is built with a wood floor, 2x4s used for floor timbers. If permanently located a concrete floor would be preferable.

Fig. 24—The J. S. Martin Colony House, as used for Regal Dorcas White Wyandottes, Port Dover, Ont., Canada. See text.

A unique feature of this house is the roost arrangement. See ground plan and roost detail in upper left and right respectively in Fig. 25. "DB" is dropping board, which is 2 ft. 6 in. deep by about 12 ft. or full width of house and placed about 2 ft. 6 in. above floor. The short roosts are designed to prevent crowding on roost at night and also to prevent fowls on rear roost rubbing tails against the wall. The roosts are made of inch stock, 3½ to 4 inches wide and 2 ft. 6 in. long, evenly spaced so that 7 roosts are provided as shown in ground plan. Each roost is dovetailed at end and fits into notched support fixed to front of dropping board, see "S,S" in plan, and fits in notch in

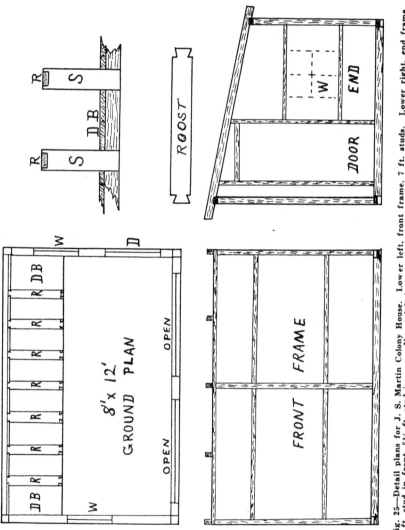

Fig. 25—Detail plans for J. S. Martin Colony House. Lower left, front frame. Lower right, end frame. 7 ft. stud in front, 5½ ft. stud in rear. Upper left is ground plan, 8 ft. deep by 12 ft. wide. "D" door. "W" windows. "DB" dropping board. "R" roosts, note short roosts dovetailed at ends to fit support and cleats. Upper right shows detail of roosts (R) and roost supports (S) and edge of dropping board (DB). Also outline of one of short roosts. See text.

cleat attached to rear studs. "S,S" roost support. "R,R" roosts. If birds start crowding on these roosts some bird has to get off. Each roost will accommodate four adult fowls or five young birds.

The joints of dovetail ends of roosts and supports are neatly made and the only fastening for the roost. To clean simply lift out roost. Kerosene applied at dovetail joints keeps roosts free from mites. The roost arrangement insures droppings falling on dropping board and also provides for ample and comfortable roosting accommodations.

This house is so simple in construction and easy to build that further detailed description seems unnecessary. It is built of common sheathing boards and covered with roofing fabric. The front curtain does not completely close in opening but leaves a space, about 6 inches by width of openings, at the top which stays open. Wire netting is used over open front and windows. It makes a good colony house but is not sufficiently deep to be built as a unit of a long continuous house.

House will accommodate 35 half grown chickens or 25 adults.

HOUSE SERIES SCORES HIT
Buzzards Bay, Mass., November 21, 1922

Dear Doctor:—How do you do it? All that Howard Hen House data —and out of your own "nut." You know more about the hanged thing than I could remember. If I build another I'll have a plan to go by and stop guessing.   Yours as ever,
                       WALTER SCOTT HOWARD.

(Note—To better appreciate this comment, be it said that Mr. Howard is a very interesting man of broad experience. While I was looking over his houses, he was keeping up a running fire of conversation and questions on topics of vital interest other than poultry. He probably did not notice the hasty sketches and notes I was making while trying to keep up my end of the talk.—P. T. W.)

CHAPTER V

Plans and Instructions for Building the Tolman Fresh-Air House, the Modified Scratch-Shed House and the Hayward-Curtiss House

"Open-air treatment has killed no one, has injured no one, has helped everyone, and determined a cure in a few. The best success is to be obtained only by facing the problem fairly and taking for a motto: 'Make everyone comfortable'."—Dr. W. P. Northrup, New York, 1908.

FOR A NUMBER of years Massachusetts has been testing open-air classes in the public schools. The city of Boston in the school year for 1921-22 had 24 such open-air classes in different parts of the city. The results have been wonderfully satisfactory.

Dr. William H. Devine, director of medical inspection, reporting on these open-air classes in "The Commonwealth" a Public Health Department publication, presents the following facts:

"The primary object of open-air classes is to improve the health of pupils.

"Physically debilitated children who are not ill to a degree to make hospital or home treatment necessary, but who are in such a lowered physical condition that the routine classroom program would be unprofitable both mentally and physically, are in these classes.

"Teachers in sympathy with the work are selected to conduct these classes. Each pupil is carefully examined by the school physician when admitted to the open-air class, and every six months thereafter. The physician visits the classes weekly. School nurse visits classes daily and visits home of each child, gives instruction concerning care of child, especially on questions of proper food, hours of sleep, fresh air in the home, and sufficient amount of rest.

"In observing the results of open-air classes, the following facts are noted: **absence of contagious diseases;** high percentage of attendance of pupils, who if they were in regular classes would be absent on account of frequent colds and other slight illnesses; ability to do the academic work of the regular grade."

The average attendance in these 24 open-air schools ranged from 93 to 99 per cent, all classes but two being above 95 per cent, three schools respectively reporting 97, 98 and 99 per cent. One school reported perfect attendance during below zero weather in February and another 99+ per cent attendance from September to February, inclusive.

Children were weighed and measured monthly, some gained 9 pounds in weight, average gain in the different schools ranged from 3 to 4¼ pounds.

When fresh-air methods will accomplish such results with "anemic, malnourished, glandular, undersized, pretubercular, also cardiac cases," children representing many nationalities including American, all improved physically and mentally, increased vigor and vitality, increased weight, better work, able to be at work practically every day and wanting to work, freedom from contagious diseases, why should anyone longer fear fresh air? Massachusetts schools, of course, supply or encourage "school lunches," wholesome food at home, cleanliness and other health habits. It pays by making better citizens.

If the poultryman will only take this plan home with him and try it on his poultry he will have better poultry and better results—comfortable quarters supplied with fresh air at all times, sufficient wholesome food in good variety and well balanced, opportunity for exercise, cleanliness, ample rest. Easy? Certainly. Less expense for buildings. Less labor. Less trouble. Better health. More eggs. More chickens. More meat. Better results all around.

Dr. W. P. Northrup points out that the secret of success with open-air methods is to "Make everyone comfortable." Editor Miller Purvis, in "Poultry," Nov. 1908, said, "The open-front poultry house is making friends all the time. It keeps fowls healthy, is cheap and **more comfortable** than the old style house."

Altho for the past 25 years the fresh-air school plan, in American cities and abroad, has been productive of only good results, the work is still confined largely to the improvement of the health of the physically unfit. Too little attention has been paid to the prevention of disease in those who for the moment enjoy good health. If half the energy and money should be expended to prevent disease that is now spent upon the cure or palliation of disease we might practically eliminate disease in a few generations. Unfortunately we have not yet reached a point where, as a people, we have ceased to be proud of our diseases or to brag about our operations. The work of preventing disease is making progress, but it is still largely confined to the few and to saving insurance companies from losses or business houses from inefficiency or loss of services thru ill health of employees. Some day we will come to look upon disease as the result of bad management and be ashamed of it rather than sympathetically considering it an unavoidable misfortune.

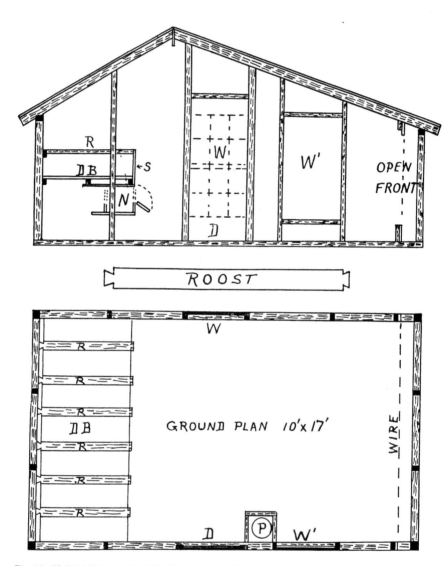

Fig. 26—Modified Tolman Fresh-Air House. Ground or floor plan, 10x17 ft., lower. Black squares locate studs. Side section view looking east, upper. About 5 ft. 6 in. high in front, 9 ft. 3 in. at peak, 5 ft. 11 in. at back. Black squares locate plates and stringers. Dropping board (DB), roosts (R), roost supports (S), nests (N), door (D), west window (W'), east window (W), water pail (P). See text.

A great many people still fear fresh air. Witness the howl that goes up when someone opens a window in a stuffy room or ill-smelling public conveyance. Many folks still hug the stove or radiator as a kitten clings to a warm hearth. Altho the open automobile has done much to improve the health of people whose work keeps them confined indoors much of the time, there is now a big scramble on for heated closed cars, which in a short time reek of bad air, human effluvia, perfumes, and the fumes of gasoline and oil. True they can be operated with windows open, and should be except in driving storms, but just notice that the occupants do not keep windows open and often run car tightly closed in mild weather.

When cold weather and winter storms prevail some folks are disposed to worry about fowls in open-front houses. There is no occasion for it. If the fowls have a good type of open-front house, have been well cared for and well fed, they will be far more comfortable than in any closed type of house that ever was devised. It is all right to say that good ventialtion can be supplied in closed houses by opening the windows, but such ventilation is seldom supplied, it is not convenient or it is too much trouble to open the windows and generally they stay closed. Where curtains are used the cloth gets damp and fills up with dust, so that in a short time the curtain is as impervious to air as a board.

The always-open-front requires no attention from the attendant, it takes care of itself. The small amount of snow that drives thru in ordinary storms causes no inconvenience and is often eaten by the fowls. They seem to prefer snow to water in winter weather. It is a very rare thing to have a blizzard which drives in enough snow to make shoveling out necessary.

Some use one-inch mesh hexagon poultry wire for protecting the open-front, but I prefer one-quarter-inch square mesh wire netting and find that it helps to keep out rain and snow. In some locations even finer wire netting might be better. For obvious reasons I use wire mosquito netting on our wide open sleeping porch, on south side of our house, and it keeps out storms very well, altho porch is open on three sides. Such netting used on a poultry house, where only the front is open, would keep out the snow and rain more effectively. The chief objection to using such fine wire for poultry house front is that it is apt to clog with dust and needs to be cleaned.

If there were no other reason for using the open-front poultry house, the fact that fowls housed therein and given good care are immune and free from contagious diseases is sufficient reason for adopting the fresh air plan. When minor colds develop, as they sometimes will—tho rarely—from one cause or another even in well cared for flocks, they are of short duration, require no treatment and never develop into serious trouble.

After a few generations of breeding poultry for health, using fresh-air brood coops and open-front houses, good feeding and common sense management, poultry diseases are conspicuous only by their absence.

The Tolman Fresh-Air House

The story of the experience of Joseph Tolman, of Rockland, Mass. was told in Chapter II. The Tolman house is an excellent fresh-air house suitable for colony houses of varying dimensions to suit the poultryman's requirements, always keeping the proportions about the same; the house being considerably deeper from back to front than it is wide, except in case of the square pattern of this house which is usually built 20x20 ft. ground plan. See outline plan, Fig. 6, in Chapter I.

Fig 26-A—Tolman house used by author for a number of years. Note shingled corners and finish beneath roof. See text.

The plan here given for 10x17 Tolman house is result of modification of original type of house by two poultrymen located in widely separated sections of the country, one in the cold north and the other in the mild south. It is a good house and gives excellent results. Operated in warm weather the door and windows are usually kept open and protected by screens of poultry netting. The front is always open for a space 3 ft. 10 in. high by the width of the house.

Fig. 26 gives ground plan (lower) and end section looking east (upper). The ground plan shows position of studs, in black on sills, door (D), east window (W), west window (W'), dropping board (DB), roosts (R). The dotted line in front marked "wire" is the always-open wire front which is located one foot back from outer edge of front sill. The sides of this house extend to limit of sills and corner posts in front, but the front itself is not boarded in. This plan with the 6 in. overhang of front roof, beyond front plate, is said to effectively keep front of house well protected from rain or snow storms. The front of house always remains open from sill to plate. The end section shows arrangement of studding, plates shown in black on top of end studs or corner posts. Frame or door (D) and for west window (W') is indicated. East window (W) is located by dotted lines. Door

Fig 26-B—Group of large Tolman houses on plant of Joseph Tolman, Rockland, Mass. These are arranged in "rights and lefts." See text.

can be arranged in east side if preferred. Dropping board (DB), roosts (R), roost support (S), nests, which slide or hook under dropping board, (N), stringers for support of dropping board and roost are indicated in black.

Between end section and ground plan in Fig. 26 is shown outline of the dovetailed roost board. This roost is made of one-inch stuff and is 4 inches wide by 4 ft. 3 in. long overall. The ends are dovetailed to fit supports in front of dropping board and stringer attached to rear studding. See description of the Martin roost in Martin Colony House, Chapter IV. The roosts are spaced same distance apart, six of them, one foot above dropping board. Each roost will accommodate seven fowls. Water pail (P) is shown in ground plan in a horizontal frame of 2x3 stuff which prevents it being overturned.

Sills on a post or stone foundation are usually 4x4s, on a concrete foundation 2x4s. Corner post studs are generally of the same dimension stuff, and other studding of 2x3s. Rafters are 2x4s.

Windows are usually two sash (6 lights each) to open up and down. Or 12 light single sash may be used and hinged at top to open out or hinged at side to open like a door. Style of windows optional with builder except that they must be built to open in summer and be closed in winter.

Ground dimensions are 10 ft. wide by 17 ft. from front to back. The wire front is one foot back from extreme front of frame, see dotted lines in plan. Front studs are 4 ft. 6 in. high; rear studs are 5 ft. Stud at rear of door is 8 ft. 4 in. Stud measurements from top of sill to bottom of plate. This gives overall dimensions of house from bottom of sill to top of roof of approximately 5 ft. 6 in. high in front, 9 ft. 3 in. at peak of roof, 5 ft. 11 in. at back. The long front reach of roof is about 12 ft. 6 in., the short reach of back roof about 7 ft. 9 in. The rafters are made of 2x4 stock and butted on an 8 in. board at peak as shown in plan. Some use two outside and two inside rafters for each reach of roof spaced equal distances apart. Others, where snowfall is heavy, prefer five rafters to each reach of roof.

Dropping board (DB) is about 4 ft. 2 in. from front to back by width of house. It is located 2 ft. 6 in. above top of sill. Bank of nests (N) is built to slide like drawer beneath dropping board, or is fastened in place with hooks and screweyes. Drop door in front to give access to nests. Roost support (S), which fastens upright to front of dropping board and supporting stringer, is made of inch stock four inches wide or a little wider. Top is notched to make snug fit with dovetail in end of roost. Rear end dovetail of roost fits in notch on horizontal stringer attached to studding. See Fig. 26 and preceding description.

Screens of one-inch mesh poultry wire over windows and a screen door of same material to use inside board door are a great convenience in operation of this house. One-inch mesh or finer is preferred as it helps to keep out sparrows and other bird pests.

Fig. 26 A shows a Tolman house used by the author for a number of years. The house is very attractive in this shingle finish. Note the shingled corners made by laying shingles to break joints and trimming to fit with draw-knife; also note shingle finish beneath roof. The house is built of 2x3 frame, covered with common boards. With shingles stained either brown or green this house fits well anywhere in the shrubbery. The house also looks well built of novelty siding. When the outside finish is of common roofing fabric it is far less attractive and by no means so lasting.

Fig. 27-C—Atherton Modification of Scratch-Shed House. Used on New Hampshire egg farm. View shows group of long houses which differ somewhat from our plans. See text.

Fig. 26 B, shows a group of large Tolman houses on Joseph Tolman's fresh air poultry plant. These houses are arranged rights and lefts and have liberal yard room.

This house is a colony house and is not suited for converting into the long continuous type of building. A long house would not get sufficient sunlight. The 10x17 size will accommodate 40 females and two males very comfortably. It can be built in smaller sizes, 6x10 and 8x14, if desired, lowering the peak a little but keeping height at front and rear about the same as in plan here given. A large house for 100 fowls may be built with square ground plan 20x20 ft., about 6 ft. high in front and rear and 10 ft. high at peak, the peak being about 7 ft. in front of rear wall. Such a house will require about twice as much window space on both sides as shown in 10x17.

For this type of house I think the 10x17 is to be preferred for convenience and all around usefulness. Where a number of houses are to be built, make them rights and lefts, part with doors in west side and others with door in east side.

Modified Scratch-Shed House

The scratch-shed house has been in use for a good many years and enjoyed a long period of popularity. It originally had an enclosed roosting room adjoining an open-front shed, the front of which was protected in bad weather by muslin or light duck curtains on frames. It was practically two houses in one, a closed house with a curtain-front shed attached. As usually operated it gave better results than the common type of closed house, but the curtains were always somewhat of a nuisance and the closed roosting room was no better than a

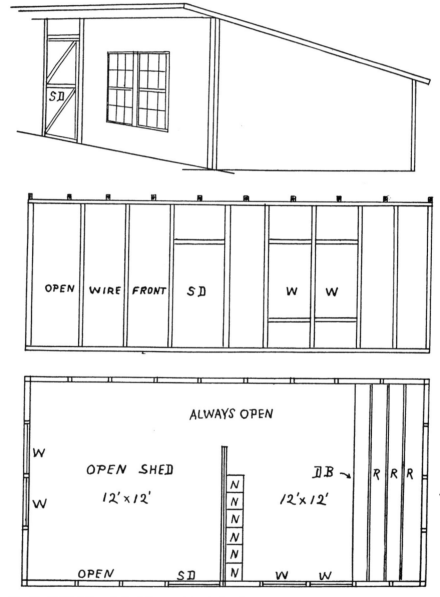

Fig. 27—Modified Scratch-Shed House. Ground plan, lower, 12x24, divided into two sections each 12x12. Left is open-front shed. right is roosting room. Door-way between sections is always open. Front frame detail, middle figure. End and part front elevation, upper. House is 9 ft. high in front, 5 ft. 6 in. high at back. Screen door in open shed front (SD), dropping board (DB), roosts (R), windows (W). Plan can be used as a single house or as unit in long house, See text.

closed house at night unless the door between it and shed was left open.

To the best of my belief the modified type of scratch-shed house, as here shown, came into being in New Hampshire and in Utah and Montana about the same time. It has proved itself a satisfactory house both in single or colony pattern and as a long continuous house. It costs more to build and is not so economical of house and ground space as some other types of building.

Fig. 27 shows plans for building the modified scratch-shed house. Ground plan, 12x24 ft. is shown at bottom of illustration. Sills and location of studs are outlined. A short partition in center divides the house into two parts each about 12x12. The right is roosting quarters, the left is scratch shed. This center partition extends from front wall to within 4 ft. of rear wall, here there is no partition and this wide door space is always open. Dropping board (DB) and roosts (R) are shown at right, nests (N) alongside partition, windows (W), two in front of roost quarters and two in west end. The open shed at left is entered by a screen door (SD) and balance of front of this shed is enclosed by wire netting. Part way curtains may be used to keep out storm but should not entirely close front at top.

Middle figure in illustration shows outline of front frame, sill, studs, plate and rafters.

At top of Fig. 27 is shown partial view of front and east end elevation. This house is about 9 ft. high in front and 5 ft. 6 in. high at rear wall. Being a simple shed roof type it is easy to build. Usually boarded in with common sheathing boards and covered with a good roofing fabric.

If built as a long continuous house make the roost quarters rights and lefts, so that two scratch sheds will come together with only a wire partition between and two roosting rooms adjoin with solid board partition between. Partition between scratch sheds can be boarded up 2½ ft. from floor or the wire covered for same distance with burlap sacking to prevent males in two pens from fighting. Water pans and feed hoppers can be arranged on this partition to supply both pens at same time.

The single 12x24 scratch-shed house as described will accommodate a flock of from 30 to 50 fowls.

Fig. 27-C shows a view of the Atherton Egg Farm, a utility White Leghorn plant, in New Hampshire mountain country. Besides these long houses this farm had 90 small colony houses of the "Hayward" type, see Fig. 28. All of these houses are open front. About 2500 layers are wintered.

Fig. 27-D—Rollins Modification of Scratch-Shed House. Inexpensive house used for exhibition Light Brahmas for many years at Westboro, Mass. Dimensions vary according to material available. House shown is 5 ft. high in front, 4 ft. in rear, 8x16 ft. floor, about 8x10 being open shed. Wire front to shed is on frame which draws out for cleaning. Door between shed and roost room always open.

This Atherton House is built up on posts to provide a runway for fowls beneath the house. I do not recommend the runway beneath house nor the low location. It differs in some other particulars from the modified scratch-shed house, Fig. 27. In this Atherton house the scratch shed is 12x14 and its open front is boarded up 2 ft. 6 in. from the bottom and down one foot from top, balance being open and protected by wire netting. The door opens into the roost room, which is 12x10. The opening between roost room and scratch shed in partition is the same as in Fig. 27 and is always open. The runway communicating with run under house is enclosed in poultry netting. The window in roosting room is one large-size half sash. In other essentials, house is the same as one shown in Fig. 27.

Fig. 27-D shows a low-built modified scratch-shed house as used by H. N. Rollins, Westboro, Mass. some sixteen to twenty years ago. The wire screen to the open front was built to slide out at end of building for convenience in cleaning the house. Light Brahmas, bred and housed in this fresh-air type of house, were famous Boston Show winners and well known to "old timers" in the fancy.

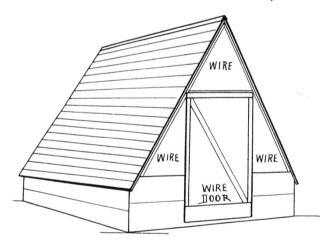

Fig. 28—The Hayward-Curtiss House. Front and side elevation. See text.

The Hayward-Curtiss House

The Hayward-Curtiss fresh-air house shown herewith in Fig. 28 is a very old type of partially open-front house. The first houses of this type, then known as the "Apex" or Hayward house, and later as the New Hampshire house, that I recall, were in use on the egg farm of C. E. L. Hayward, Hancock, N. H. from about 1885 to 1905. J. H. Curtiss, veteran grower of and wholesale dealer in South Shore soft roasters, Assinippi, Mass. used a similar house to some extent for

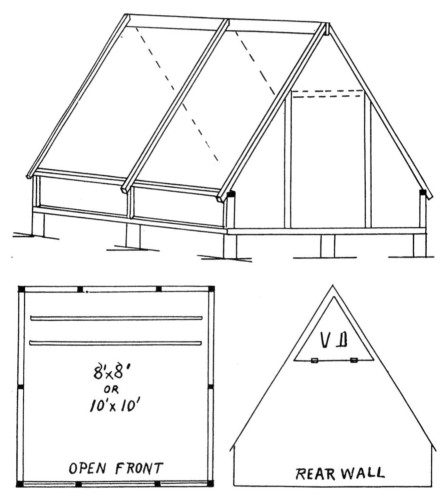

Fig. 29—Detail Hayward-Curtiss House. Frame plan, upper. Ground plan, lower left. Rear wall, lower right. This house may be built either 8x8 or 10x10 ground plan. Black squares lo-cate short studs. House is 8 ft. high at peak, 1½ ft. high at sides, measured from top of sill. Position of roosts, when used, is located in ground plan. A ventilating door, about 3 ft. wide at base and 2½ ft. high (VD in plan), in apex of rear wall is used in summer. See text.

Fig. 30—Group of Hayward-Curtiss Houses as used for a number of years on plant of J. H. Curtiss, Assinippi, Mass. See text.

many years. As a small colony house, portable or permanent, the type has been and is still popular all thru New England on both fancy and utility poultry farms. Some farms have a considerable number of these small houses which are scattered about the fields in summer and grouped, company street style, near farm buildings in winter.

Some are built with shingled roofs, some with novelty siding and some of common boards covered with roofing fabric. Some have board floors, some have dirt floors only. Those with tight board floors are best for young stock, the dirt floor affords no protection against rats. Some have floors built in, others have removable floors, similar to house described in Chapter III. Fig. 28 shows side and front elevation. Except for boarding to just above eaves at bottom the front is practically all wire netting.

Fig. 29 at lower left shows ground plan, studs indicated in black and position of roosts shown. There is no dropping board. At lower right is shown elevation of rear wall. In apex is a ventilating door (VD) used to make a cooler house in summer. This is covered with wire netting when door is open. At top of Fig. 29 is shown frame plan with position of posts indicated, if house is to sit on posts. Usually it is preferable to make this type of house portable. Any available material will serve, usually the framing is 2x4s for sills and 2x3s for balance of frame. Fig. 30 shows a row of these houses used for Light Brahma capons on farm of J. H. Curtiss, Assinippi, Mass. The door has one-quarter inch square mesh wire netting over open portion. I prefer to have practically all of front end of this house open as shown in Fig. 28.

This house is 1 ft. 6 in. high at eaves, about 8 ft. high at peak of roof. The construction is easy and does not call for more detailed instructions.

A house of this type will make very comfortable quarters for a small breeding pen or for a flock of growing chicks on range. The 8x8 house of this type will accommodate 10 to 15 fowls. The 10x10 accommodates 25 layers. On Mr. Hayward's New Hampshire egg farm, years ago, it was customary to fill such houses up with layers and keep them confined to the house thru the season, selling them off alive to market when they let up on egg production.

Mr. Hayward's fowls were watered in summer, in winter they were given snow to take place of water. Tho closely confined the hens were healthy and the egg yield good. Many egg farmers favored the plan.

FRESH-AIR FLOCKS HAPPY AND CONTENT

George A. Cosgrove, who has had fifty years poultry experience, answering two correspondents who think that open-front houses may be cruel, in August "Rural New-Yorker," 1924, says:

"Both these poultrymen think the open-front poultry house is cruel, or at least uncomfortable for hens; and **they are mistaken.** * * * *

"The cold here reaches 10 to 12 degrees below zero every Winter, and I have known it 20 below. The hens in these open-front houses lay well all winter.

"I think that hens kept in these open-front houses are hardier, more enduring and less liable to disease than those kept in tight houses, and if anyone should open the door of one of those houses on a Winter day and listen to the noise of those singing, cackling hens, as I have, he would have no doubt of their perfect content and happiness."

CHAPTER VI

Comfortable and Cheerful Homes for Fowls—Plans and Instructions for Building Woods' Semi-Monitor Open-Front Poultry Houses—10x16 House for 40 Fowls—Large Colony House, 20x20 for 100 Fowls—Long Type

"Fresh air has a hardening effect upon fowls and an overdose has never been known to cause serious trouble. * * * The principle of ventilation in the open-front house is the same as blowing smoke out of a bottle; instead of strong currents there is a quiet diffusion of air with the least possible draft. This type of house has proven successful in every climate, and may now be spoken of as **the modern poultry house which has come to stay.** It is one big step toward placing the poultry industry on a firm and lasting foundation."— C. L. Opperman, 1910.

SINCE THE BUILDING of the first Woods' open-front poultry house in 1908 for experimental purposes and later publication of plans and results, buildings of this type have been in use in all climates with excellent results. The house is comfortable, cheerful for the fowls and convenient for the poultry keeper.

There have been many requests for information concerning any changes or improvements which my long experience with this house may have led me to make or suggest. Such changes and improvements, which are mainly with a view to greater simplicity, economy in construction, convenience of the operator and comfort of the fowls at all seasons, are brought right up to date in this chapter. Because many beginners, not alone with poultry but with amateur carpentry, will wish to make use of these house plans, certain details of construction shown in the illustrations are explained more fully than would be necessary for those with more experience.

Do not be afraid to build and use an open-front house. When using one do not let the imagination conjure up troubles which do not exist. In other words, do not get panicky and get "cold feet." There are some folks in this world who, whenever they meet with an idea new to them, lose their nerve and let their "feet freeze up to the knees." It is fortunate that there are lots of people who are not "Cold-feetos." Bear in mind that fowls are provided with thick overcoats of feathers and ample undergarments of fluff, and they can't "take 'em off" at will. Nature provides only for such change of garments as is suited to the seasons. H. G. Wells says, "Feathers are the distinctive covering of birds, and they give a power of resisting heat and cold far greater than that of any other integumentary covering except perhaps the thickest fur." Keep that in mind—with the possible exception of the thickest fur, feathers have far greater power to resist cold than any other skin covering. That ought to prevent "cold feet" but if it isn't sufficient, remember the titmouse and consider other happy small birds that winter out of doors about our homes and in woodland. (See Chapter I).

An Expert's Opinion

James B. Morman, who has made a study of poultry houses and qualified as a poultry expert, says of the Woods house :—

"To keep fowls in such a house in climates where the thermometer may drop from zero to 40 degrees below would seem to many poultry keepers the height of folly, because it might seem to risk the health and comfort of the fowls. That has been one of the great mistakes of the poultry industry. The fact is that a house constructed on this principle, if made sufficiently long from front to back, say 18 to 20 feet or more, is not only highly comfortable, but affords the best protection to the fowls against drafts while providing them with abundance of necessary fresh air. No matter how hard the wind may blow, it cannot penetrate any great depth into the interior of such a house. During one of the worst wind and rain storms ever experienced in Plymouth County, Mass., Dr. Woods says, in regard to his open-front poultry house, that 'the wind could not be felt at all in the house at a distance of four feet from the open front. The fowls were comfortable and happy. A little water came in thru the wire screen, but only a very little, and less than one yard of the floor immediately back of the wire front screen receiving a wetting.' * * * * *

"A strong wind blowing against the front of an open-front poultry house is met and overcome by a perfect air cushion on the inside, which turns back the wind, no matter how strong it may blow. Therefore, every poultry house should be carefully constructed with a view to establishing and maintaining such a condition. Major P. H. Falkner, a British authority on poultry house construction and ventilation, says that 'the Woods type of open-front poultry house is perfect in this respect, for, altho it has a skilfully placed window behind the open front, there is no draft as regards the sleeping quarters.' * * * * *

"This method of open-front poultry house construction seems practically perfect from both the hygienic and physical points of view. It furnishes a bountiful supply of free atmospheric oxygen and successfully carries off the exhaled and poisonous carbonic acid gas.

"The open-front poultry house aims to provide open-air conditions without their disadvantages. When all the features of the Woods type of house are taken into consideration, it is evident that it is very satisfactory and has come to stay. If fowls are housed upon this plan they ought to lay more eggs than fowls sheltered in closed houses; the fowls ought to live longer, because they are far less subject to weakening conditions and are thereby made less susceptible to diseases when kept in open-front houses; and the chickens hatched from eggs laid under these conditions ought to thrive, because they are the progeny of healthy parents."

There is not space enough available to permit the use of the many testimonials which have been received from satisfied users of the Woods house during the past fifteen years. As the "proof of the pudding is in the eating" so the proof of a house is in the results from practical use of it; also in the fact that experienced poultrymen after building one, build more. E. B. Thompson, prominent Barred Rock fancier, built and used one, then built more. F. W. Floyd, proprietor of a practical farm in Michigan, was a pioneer in that state to build a Woods house, soon after first plans were published. He liked it so well that he built a number of colony houses and a long continuous house of same type. After the world war Mr. Floyd moved to eastern New York and wrote me to know if I had made any changes or improvements in the house since he first built as he was about to build more of them on his new place.

A personal letter from H. H. Stoddard, veteran pioneer poultry editor, in 1910, containing a long and enthusiastic account of fresh air experience with poultry, includes the following:

"Shake, Doctor! You are in it! I don't know whether you stop to pat yourself on the back very much or not, but it is fair to presume that it is pleasant for you to reflect that now, and for ages, thousands and millions and billions of pairs of lungs will push and pull a volume of fresh air, minus carbon dioxide, that will equal a volume of the atmosphere over an empire, and a wave of good hearty animal happiness will roll, like the British drumbeat encircling the earth and ceasing not so long as there is civilization and the keeping of domestic animals! I write with some ardor on this fresh air biz for reasons I will proceed to set down. For fifteen years or more I read nothing on poultry. Lost the run of things entirely. Then read R. P. J. files thru 1909. Learned more of importance, I can truthfully say, from your pen than from all my previous reading of poultry books and papers put together."

And so it goes thru a whole chest full of letters from poultrymen and poultry women all over our own country and many foreign lands.

Let a successful woman in my own state have the last word on this subject here, Mrs. J. W. Dwinell, Topsfield, Mass., says:

"The question of housing is equally as important as feeding, and we strongly advocate the open-air house. We have used both the open and closed houses, and know from actual experience that the open house will give the best results, both in fertility of eggs and in the health of the birds. Notwithstanding the heavy winter egg yield from our birds, we have had fine results in hatching, the eggs being 85 to 90 per cent fertile. We attribute this in a great measure to the open-air housing. We have two types of open-air houses, but find the Dr. Woods house the better, in that it admits more sunlight, thus keeping the litter sweet and dry for a longer period, and it affords better ventilation in summer."

Fig. 31—Woods' 20x20 Colony House, front elevation. Photo taken on author's farm after severe March blizzard. Note the cheerful flock of S. C. White Leghorns seen thru the wire of the open front. The big cock with tail and head up is just crowing to show how cheerful he is.

Snow and the Open-Front House

The Woods house is a semi-monitor type. One pessimistic critic has frequently expressed the opinion that accumulations of snow on the short reach of front roof would prove troublesome and obstruct the monitor windows. During the winter of 1915-16 in an article entitled "Not a Good Season for the Woods' House," this critic sneeringly referred to such houses as "cheerful places for fowls," assuming that the houses would be dark and dreary. Unwittingly he voiced a truth, for the Woods houses are unquestionably **"cheerful places for fowls,"** especially in stormy weather.

March 1916 was that year pronounced by the weather bureau "the snowiest March on record." We had a big blizzard, a succession of snow storms, very deep snow, and on the first clear day I took a number of photographs of my houses to show snow on roof. In no case was there snow enough to obstruct the windows, nor did snow blow thru the wire front in sufficient amount to be troublesome. Even in cold Quebec with snow 4 ft. deep on a level and very deep in drifts, one Woods house user wrote that the snow had not caused any inconvenience other than such as would be experienced with any type of house and that the fowls were comfortable and happy.

In February 1920, a most difficult winter all thru, we had a big blizzard of heavy wet snow. This was followed by a freeze and more snow. Snow, rain and freeze followed each other in rapid succession. Our roads were all blocked with snow above the top of cordwood by the roadside. No trains, no mail, no newspapers for days, no trolley cars for weeks. We had to go for supplies dragging a hand sled and wearing snow shoes. In our field there was snow to the top of the

Fig. 32—West end and front elevation of another Woods 20x20 house on author's farm. Photo taken after a heavy snow storm. See text.

pasture fence and a young orchard was completely buried. We had to shovel the snow from our piazza roof, but, altho some of our semi-monitor houses carried a heavy load of snow, we did not shovel it off as the top windows were not obstructed enough to shut off much light. We had nine 20x20 and three 10x16 semi-monitor houses. From one house, in an exposed location, we had to remove a little snow from one corner inside of the open front, but chiefly because that house was then occupied by a brood sow nearly ready to farrow. I was surprised to note that so little snow had gone thru the wire front or piled up on the roof, for our sleeping porch, on the south side of our dwelling, took in considerable snow. The "air cushion" in the poultry houses must have been working well, for altho there was a big drift in front of some houses there was considerable open space between the drift and the wire front, sufficient to give a clear way for ample light and air. "Cheerful places for fowls?" I'll say that they are.

Woods' Large Colony House

Per head of fowls housed a square house is probably the least expensive to build. For housing layers or for big flocks to produce incubator eggs I like the large size colony house.

The large colony house of Woods type is made 20x20 ft. It will comfortably house 100 hens and 4 or 5 males. I have carried as high as 150 fowls of American and Mediterranean breeds in such houses, with good results, but the smaller number is to be preferred, especially if it is necessary to keep the fowls confined to the house much of the time.

My own houses are built with earth floors, but concrete floors would be much better. I used low priced lumber for boarding in and covered sides and roof with shingles. If I were to build again I should

Fig. 33—One of author's 20x20 open-front houses, west end and front elevation, summer view. This house is built of matched boards. The chickens are early hatched White Plymouth Rocks. Photo taken in August 1911.

prefer to make a concrete foundation, erect frame on that and cover in with novelty siding, shiplap or matched boards, using asbestos shingles on roof. As suggested in earlier chapter it is advisable to look over the available lumber in your own locality and make a selection of whatever seems to be the best value for the money and is suited to the purpose.

Fig. 31 shows front elevation of one of my 20x20 houses, photo taken after the March blizzard in 1916. It will be noted that there is not much snow on the roof nor in front of house. The cheerful flock in the front of house is part of 80 yearling White Leghorns. The cock with head and tail up was crowing just as the camera clicked. Fig. 32 is another of my large houses in the woods, photo taken after same storm, view shows west and south front elevation. Fig. 33 is

Fig. 34—Group of three connecting 20x20 Woods houses on plant of E. B. Thompson, Amenia, N. Y., breeder of famous Imperial "Ringlet" Barred Plymouth Rocks. See text.

still another of my houses, this one built of matched boards, showing south front and west side and part of a flock of White Plymouth Rock youngsters.

Fig. 34 shows front and side view of a group of three connecting 20x20 houses built on a side hill on the plant of E. B. Thompson, breeder of the famous Imperial "Ringlet" Barred Plymouth Rocks, Amenia, N. Y. Note that these houses are placed on a "terraced" foundation of concrete, keeping each house on a level foundation and saving expense of much grading.

Fig. 35 shows ground plan of 20x20 Woods house. The outside sills are 4x4s. The middle sill also is a 4x4. A solid partition between roosts extends from this sill to roof and for a distance of 8 ft. from the back wall. That portion of middle sill which is shown in outline and not shaded is flush with floor and has no partition above it. As this middle sill carries a good deal of weight it must have a solid foundation under it. The studs are shown in black squares on sills. The three main studs (large black squares) support the monitor and should be 4x4s or made of two 2x4s spiked together. Door (D), windows (W), roosts (R), nests (N) and water pail on raised platform (P), poultry door or slide (S) are indicated on ground plan. Corner studs and studs at both ends of middle partition should be 2x4s. Balance of studding 2x3s.

Fig. 36 is end section view of 20x20 house looking west, giving frame detail. Rafters are indicated by name, also the sill. Main stud is also marked. Usually there are nine rafters in front and same number in back, all 2x4s. The outer plates (P) shown in black on top of studs are made of 2x4 stuff. "A" is rear plate of front roof, spiked to main studs. Spiked to this plate between the main studs and toe-nailed to them are fitted long pieces of 2x4 to stiffen support of mon-

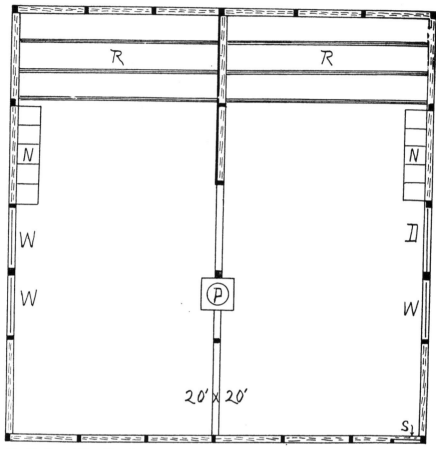

Fig. 35—Ground Plan Woods' 20x20 Large Colony Open-Front House. Windows (W), door (D), nests (N), roosts (R), water pail (P), hen door or slide (S). See text.

itor and roof, position is shown in outline on stud. "B" is a brace plate of 2x4 stuff made to engage the under side of three or four rafters and at right angles to them. "C" shown in dotted lines is a 2x4 stud at end of middle partition which supports brace plate (B). "W" shows location of east window. Dotted lines indicate position of the two west windows. This improved house differs from my old house in having larger windows. These side windows are each two sash, six lights 8x12 in. There are 4 monitor windows (W') hinged at the top to swing out as shown. "I" is the strap iron which serves as window rod or bracket, (See Chapter III). Door (D), nests (N), roosts (R). On either side of each monitor window is a 2x3 stud from plate "A" to top plate (P), between these studs, at top and bottom of window opening are string pieces of 2x3.

The bank of nests is on side wall about 3 ft. above sill. It is a good plan to make cover or roof of the nest boxes on a sharp slant to discourage roosting on top of nests. "F" is the always open front, the dotted lines show position of studs.

It will be noted that no dropping boards are shown. I do not use a dropping board in this house or in my regular type 10x16. Unless a dropping board is cleaned daily it is a good deal of a nuisance. I prefer to have the free open space beneath the roosts. The scratching of the fowls will carry litter and sand back under the roosts and keep the droppings from becoming objectionable. Simply clean out the whole floor when the litter is changed. The only house on my farm in which I use a dropping board is the 10x16 portable type shown in Chapter III. I had that house factory built, knock-down style, and the dropping board came with it. In so light a framed house the board served to help stiffen the building so I retained it.

If the reader will take a piece of cardboard and make for himself a paper scale, marking it off in feet and inches according to dimensions given for the plans, he will get better satisfaction out of the illustrations. All of the drawings were made to scale when drawn and have been reduced in varying dimensions to suit space in publication, but it should be easy to make a paper scale for each plan.

The 20x20 house, shown in end section view in Fig. 36, has front and rear studs which measure just 5 ft. each from top of sill to bottom

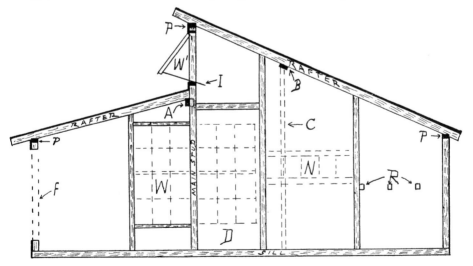

Fig. 36—Woods' 20x20 House, end section elevation, view looking west. Rear plate for front roof (A), note outline on main stud of 2x4 spiked to this plate (see text), other roof plates (P); middle brace plate under rafters (B), partition end stud (C), supporting brace plate (B), door (D), nests (N), roosts (R), always-open-front (F), dotted lines indicate stud; east window location (W), two west windows located by dotted lines; monitor top window (W'), window rod (I).

of plate. The main stud, supporting monitor, is 10 ft. 4 in. from top of sill to bottom of plate ; this gives an overall dimension from bottom of sill to top of roof, along line of front of main stud, of 11 ft. 3 in. Overall measure front and rear, along outer side of studs from bottom of sill to top of roof, is 5 ft. 11 in. Measuring along top of sill from outer edge of rear stud (inside black line) to back side of main stud the distance is just 12 ft. From same point on main stud to outer edge of front stud (inside black line) is just 8 ft. Measuring along front side of main stud from top of sill to top of plate (A), just 7 ft. From top of sill to bottom of string piece for top of door, 6 ft. 6 in. It is 4 inches from top of front roof to bottom of opening for monitor window, and 6 inches from top of window to bottom of rafter. The window is 2 ft. 4 in. high—a half sash. There are 4 half sash, 6 light monitor windows in each house. Measured along the front side the stud at rear of door is 9 ft. The width of door between this stud and main stud is 3 ft. Bottom of lower window string piece is 1 ft. above top of sill. Roosts are 2 ft. 9 in. from bottom of roost to top of sill. Rear rafters are 14 ft. 10 in. long. Front rafters are 8 ft. 11 in. long. The always open front (F)—to be covered with one-quarter inch square mesh wire netting—is 4 ft. 2 in. high by the width of the house. Dotted lines show outline of front stud at open front (F). A hen door or slide is usually provided at right side of front, about 15 in. wide by 18 in. high (S) Fig. 35.

Work out these dimensions on plan with a home made paper scale—cut one twice length of the rear stud from top of sill to bottom of plate, mark this into ten equal parts, each part represents a foot, divide one section into 12 equal parts representing inches—and there should be no difficulty in following all measurements in Fig. 36. It may be necessary to make a scale in similar fashion for each drawing owing to slight differences in reduction of originals for reproduction. It should be easy to take a known dimension and work up a paper scale from it. In case of the black squares indicating studs and plates, etc., there may be some variation, due to a variety of causes, but it need not cause any inconvenience—besides dimension stuff used for framing varies quite a little and you have to allow for it and keep tabs on the measurements of material used.

Anyone who can build a house can make good use of the plans and dimensions given in this book. Simply study the illustrations and text and "use the old bean" as my boy says. Don't read hastily and then hurry to write a letter to the author or publisher. Work out the plans for yourself, modify them a little to accommodate them to the available material if necessary. We have tried to make this easy for the beginner and hope that we have succeeded.

Provide screens of inch mesh wire netting for inside of all windows.

Woods' 10x16 Colony House

The 20x20 house just described is a fine house for a large farm flock, for the practical plant, or wherever it may be desirable to carry flocks in units of 100. It is a safe house whether operated at capacity or for a small flock. I have taken presumably tender birds, like Faverolles and S. C. Leghorns, in single pens 4 females and a male, direct from the shipping coop and wintered them in these large houses. The fowls gave good results and enjoyed good health. Except for experimental purposes, of course, it is not good economy to use so large a house for a small flock.

Fig. 37—Woods' 10x16 Open-Front House on author's farm. Photo taken after March blizzard. At time house contained a pen of four Black Langshans which arrived from Pacific coast in February after a nine-day journey. Fowls did not have to be acclimated and gave fine results. See text.

For all around use for the fancier, the breeder who uses small flock units, the back-lotter, or anyone who requires a medium sized colony house, the regular type Woods 10x16 open-front house serves the purpose better. Houses from four to forty fowls.

Fig. 37 is a view of a 10x16 house on my farm which has been in use for 12 years. It is the early pattern but is a very satisfactory house. Photo was taken after a March snow storm. At the time the house contained a pen of valuable Black Langshans, three females

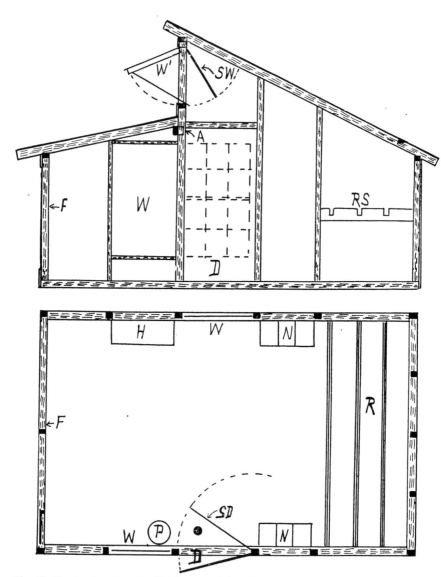

Fig. 38—Construction plans for Woods' 10x16 Colony Open-Front House. Ground plan (lower). End section elevation. (Upper) "A" 2x4 plate for rear of front roof (in black), note outline on main stud of second 2x4 spiked to plate "A." "D" door; "F" location of always-open-front, open space is 4 ft. 2 in. high by width of house; "H" dry mash hopper; "N" nests; "R" roosts; "SD" screen door; "SW" screen window; "RS" roost support; "W" windows; "W'" monitor window. See text.

and a male, which arrived from the Pacific coast in February after a nine-day journey during which they had been roughly used and nearly starved. These birds did not have to get acclimated, they went right to work and gave fine results.

Fig. 38 is building plan for the improved 10x16 house. The ground plan (lower) shows sills, studs (black squares), nests (N), feed hopper (H), water pail (P), roosts (R), windows (W), solid outer door (D), inner screen door (SD), location open front (F). The house is 10 ft. wide by 16 ft. from back to front. Detail side section plan is shown above. "A" shows 2x4 rear plate for front roof and outline of additional 2x4 which is spiked to the plate between the main studs supporting monitor. The plate is 2x4, as also is the main stud at either side of house. (See plan of 20x20 house Fig. 36).

The sill in this end elevation plan, from inner side of boarding indicated at front and back, is just 16 ft. Use this as basis of making home-made paper scale as recommended earlier in this chapter. From outside of rear stud to back of main stud is 10 ft., from there to front of front stud is 6 ft. The front and back studs (or corner posts) are 5 ft. each from top of sill to bottom of plate. From top of sill to bottom of plate "A" is 6 ft. Main stud is 9 ft. 10 in. from top of sill to bottom of top plate. It is 6 in. from top of front roof to bottom of monitor window; 4 in. from top of window to bottom of rafter. Window (W') is 2 ft. 4 in. high and is a half sash. Two of these windows are used in the monitor top.

The monitor windows are hinged at the top to swing out and held in place by a strap iron rod or window bracket. Usually the monitor windows are kept open from April or May 1st until snow flies in fall. In winter they are kept shut at night and only opened by day during mild sunny weather when house warms up a good deal. A screen window (SW), of inch mesh poultry wire, is provided to protect monitor window and keep out small birds. It is hinged at top to swing in.

In end elevation plan (upper) Fig. 38, the west window is indicated by dotted lines, east window (W), door (D), roost support (RS), 2 ft. 6 in. from top of sill to bottom of roost support. "F" indicates the front stud and always-open-front, the opening, which is protected only by one-quarter inch square mesh wire netting, is 4 ft. 2 in. high by the width of the house. The front is always open, no curtains are ever used anywhere in these Woods houses.

The overall dimensions of the 10x16 house are 5 ft. 11 in. from bottom of sill to top of roof along line of stud both back and front, 10 ft. 9 in. from bottom of sill to top of roof along front line of main stud.

Fig. 39—Long Woods' House on plant of E. B. Thompson, Amenia, N. Y. House is 50 ft. long with grain room 10 ft. wide built on at right end. Since photo was taken Mr. Thompson has added enough sections to make the house 120 ft. long. See text.

The bottom of the front has a board 10 in. wide from bottom of sill up, and is boarded down to 6 in. below rafters. There are five rear rafters 12 ft. 9 in. long and five front rafters 7 ft. long, all 2x4s. Main studs and plates are 2x4s, other studs and roosts 2x3s.

In hot summer weather the house may be operated with all windows and doors open, which gives a very cool and comfortable hot weather house. With windows and door closed it is comfortable for any size flock from four to forty fowls in severe winter weather.

Woods' House Long Type

Either the 20x20 or the 10x16 Woods' houses will serve as units in a long continuous house. Whichever size is adopted as the unit I would suggest that it would be a good plan to make the wire fronts on frames to bolt in, so that they can be taken out when cleaning house. If yards are arranged so that a wagon can be driven along in front of the house at cleaning time, it will be easier to shovel out litter, etc., directly into the wagon. If this is not done, then some sort of rail carrier should be provided thru connecting doors from pen to pen to take litter out and in. The colony type house can be readily cleaned thru doors and open windows. Both sizes of house have been successfully used for units of long houses. For all around purposes except on large practical plants and egg farms, I believe the 10x16 unit has the wider range of usefulness. Personally, as I have stated before, I prefer the colony house.

Fig. 39 shows a long Woods house as built by E. B. Thompson, Amenia, N. Y., to house his Imperial "Ringlets." The house as shown in photo is 16 ft. from back to front and has five pens, making it 50 ft. long; at the right end is a feed room 10 ft. wide containing five bins. The house is built on a concrete foundation and has a concrete land-

ing in front of grain room. Since the photo was taken, Mr. Thompson writes me under date of August 26, 1922, more sections have been
added to this house making it 120 ft. long. Fig. 40 shows end view of
this house. A house that is good enough for "Ringlets," bred for exhibition quality, ought to be good enough for any fowl whether kept
for fancy or utility purposes.

Fig. 41 gives ground plan (lower) of three sections of a long
Woods house built of 10x16 units. The front and east end elevation
(upper) is perspective diagram not drawn to scale. The ground plan
is by scale. Roosts (R), nests (N), window (W), outside door to
swing out (D), inside doors on patent hinges to swing both ways (D'),
dry mash hopper supplying two pens (H), water pan supplying two
pens (P). Hen doors or slides (S). Studs indicated on ground plan
in black. This house carries one more stud in front of each section

Fig. 40—End view of long Woods house on plant of E. B. Thompson,
Amenia, N. Y. Shows concrete landing in front of grain room and
house door, also concrete foundation. See text.

than the colony house to give greater strength to long stretch of front
roof. Fig. 42 gives detail partitions in this long house. There is a
solid partition (upper) every 20 ft. which prevents wind from getting
a long sweep thru house such as would occur if wire partitions were
used thru whole length. The intermediate partition (lower) which is
part matched boards and part wire, is used midway between solid partitions. Built into this partition is a dry mash hopper (H) to supply
two pens and a shelf with water pan (P) to supply two pens. Nests
(N), roosts and roost supports (R). Matched board door (D) in solid
partition and door of wire netting, bottom half covered with burlap
(D') in intermediate partition are shown. These doors should be hung
on patent hinges to swing both ways, stops provided to hold door
closed, and hand holes provided in doors to operate stops. The hand

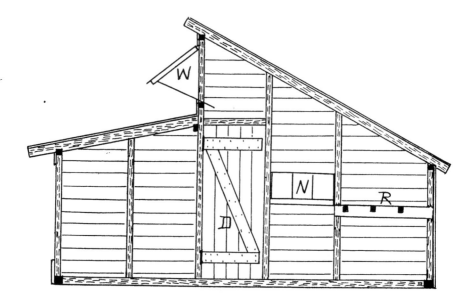

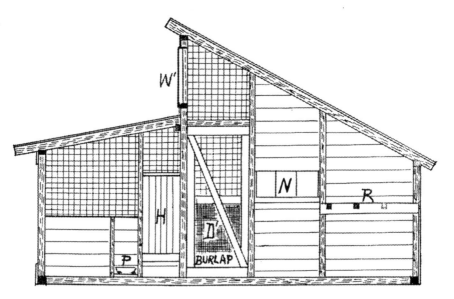

Fig. 42—Plan of partitions and studding, long type of Woods house. Upper plan is solid partition used every 20 ft. of house length. Lower plan is intermediate partition, midway between solid partitions and is part wire as shown. The doors in these partitions are made to swing both ways. "D'" door of wire and burlap in intermediate partition. "D" matched board door in solid partition, "H" dry mash hopper built in to supply two pens, "N" nests, "P" water pan on shelf in partition to supply two pens, "R" roosts and roost support, "W" monitor window open, "W'" monitor window closed. See text.

hole in solid door (D) should be provided with wicket or shutter. These partition plans indicate frame in shaded lines. They are drawn to scale and reader should make paper scale to check up measurements. The rear stud is 4 ft. 6 in. from top of sill to bottom of plate. Front stud is 5 ft. from top of sill to bottom of plate. Main stud, 10 ft. from rear wall, is 9 ft. 10 in. high from top of sill to bottom of plate (black square under rafter at peak). Rear rafter is 12 ft. 9 in. long, front rafter is 7 ft. 4 in. long. These rafters are 2x4s and are spaced about 2½ ft. apart. They are lightly notched to fit plates.

Do not make a deep notch in rafters, it wastes the strength that the timber is used for. In cutting rafters or studs, where several have to be made the same length, do not lay the first one cut on top of piece of timber and use it as guide to saw by. If this is done each piece of timber will be a little longer than the other. Measure off a place on the work bench the length desired and nail a block at left end, at right end use a miter-box (see any good dictionary) to hold saw at exact angle desired. Run your timber thru the miter-box and

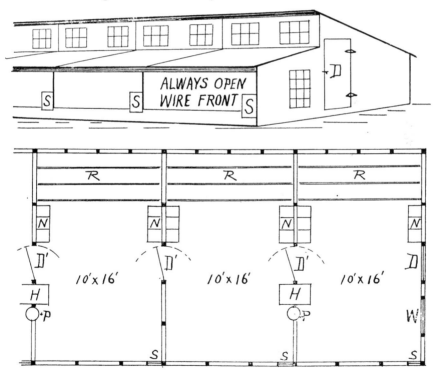

Fig. 41—Long Type of Woods Open-Front House. 10x16 units. Ground plan (lower), east end and front elevation (upper). "D" door, "D'" partition doors to swing both ways, "H" feed or dry mash hopper, "N" nests, "P" water pan, "R" roosts, "S" poultry door or slide. See text.

butt it against the block at left, then saw off in miter-box and each piece will duplicate the other.

In Fig. 42 the monitor window is shown open (W) in upper plan and closed (W') in lower. There are two monitor windows in each 10 ft. section of house length. These windows are six-light half sash, 8x12 glass.

In all of these semi-monitor houses there are 2x3 studs on either side of each window opening, with 2x3 stringers above and below window opening. These monitor studs extend from top of 2x4 spiked to plate "A" (See Figs. 36 and 38) to bottom of top plate (P) and serve to stiffen and support monitor and roof.

In other details the units of this long house are essentially the same as the regular colony type 10x16 house. The rear wall may be made same height as in colony house if desired. In the long house the partitions take place of side walls of colony house, the outside walls of the long house at each end should for convenience have door and window as shown in elevation Fig. 41.

The dimensions recommended for these houses should be observed quite closely. The Woods house has been built as small as 10 ft. from front to back and 6 ft. wide, and the owner is pleased with it. For best results I would advise houses that are not less than 16 ft. from front to back.

The manner of framing given herein is not arbitrary. In viewing dwellings, barns, poultry houses, etc. in various sections of the country, I find that different builders use widely differing plans for building the frame of a structure. The chief essentials are to provide a good solid foundation; on this erect a frame sufficiently substantial to make a strong building that will withstand the wear and tear of winds and storms, get enough support under the roof to enable it to support the heaviest weight of snow which may be expected.

No dropping board is shown in the long house. I prefer to do without one as in the colony house. This is optional with the builder. If a dropping board is desired, provide one 2½ ft. above top of sill and make it wide enough to catch all droppings. It is well to have roosts about six inches to a foot above dropping board.

Before attempting to build read entire chapter. All Woods houses are essentially the same; you may find details in description of one type which will help you to a better understanding of the others.

CHAPTER VII

Notes on Curtain Fronts—Plans and Instructions for Building the Gillette House, the Lord Farms Leghorn House and the Stoddard Southern House for Hot Climates

"I was a warm house advocate at first, but when I saw the good effects of the open house I adopted it and I would not go back to the closed house. I have tried open-front houses over twelve years, so am in a position to judge."—C. Bricault, M. D. V., Haverhill, Massachusetts.

FOR MANY YEARS well and favorably known to the poultry fancy, Dr. C. Bricault bred White Wyandottes and devoted himself to combining Standard beauty qualifications with persistent heavy laying. His bred-to-lay strain was among the better known of the early families of prolific egg producers.

A successful veterinary surgeon of more than ordinary ability, he was among the first to appreciate the value and possibilities of fresh-air housing for poultry. After experimenting with several types of houses including the scratching-shed, he designed and built what he called the "New Idea Poultry House," a long shed-roofed house of simple construction, divided into pens 10x12 ft. each. In the front of each pen was a large window and a Dutch door, a door divided horizontally in the middle so that one half may be open while the other is shut. The upper part of the Dutch door was made of coarse muslin. It proved to be a very good house. Later on he became interested in the open-front house and adopted it. His opinion of the open-front house is quoted at head of this chapter.

Writing about poultry houses in 1902, Dr. Bricault said:—

"The building of poultry houses is an important event to the poultry keeper, for mistakes made at this point are costly ones, as we have learned from experience. Our first house was what is called a closed house with one window in south front of every pen, and an alleyway at back. We never liked this house; it would frost up on cold days, get damp, and the alleyway was the cause of making it drafty, and drafts in a poultry house are the cause of much sickness. We could not ventilate the house as much as we would have liked, without making a draft.

"The next house we built was an open-scratching-shed house,

nearly 300 ft. long. This was indeed a great improvement over the closed house but it had some disadvantages.

"We are firm believers in fresh air for our hens. We have had ample opportunity to note its good effects upon the health of the stock and the egg yield."

About a dozen years later, while attending the big Boston Show, Dr. Bricault and myself had a long talk on the subject of the benefits of fresh-air, more particularly as applied to poultry and other domestic animals. His experience had convinced him that ample fresh air both day and night increased normal resistance and prevented disease. He told of success in treating sick horses and cattle by fresh-air methods, suitable food and good care; said that he was using drugs less and less, and devoting more attention to providing comfortable fresh air living conditions and to good feeding and good care. He was sure that application of common sense methods along these lines would to a large extent eliminate diseases of poultry and other domestic animals.

Dr. Oliver Wendell Holmes, many years ago, said: "There are three wicks you know to the lamp of a man's life: brain, blood and breath. Press the brain a little, its light goes out, followed by the others. Stop the heart a minute, and out go all three of the wicks. Choke the air out of the lungs, and presently the fluid ceases to supply the other centers of flame, and all is soon stagnation, cold, and darkness."

Recent investigations in the scientific world emphasize how much these "three wicks" of the lamp of life depend upon an abundant supply of fresh air for breathing purposes both night and day. The lungs of man, fowl, or beast, cannot function properly unless supplied with an ample amount of fresh air at all times. Upon the proper functioning of the lungs, normal aeration of the blood, depend health, growth, resistance to disease, normal reproduction—life itself. Many obscure diseases have been traced back to defective functioning of lungs, from one cause or another, which may, in brief, be attributed to an insufficient supply of pure fresh air to keep blood and tissues in good active natural condition. Living under open air conditions encourages deep breathing and deep breathing of wholesome open air gives all parts of the respiratory system opportunity to function properly.

Curtain Fronts

In my own houses I do not use any curtains (muslin on frames) for the open fronts. I do not consider the curtains necessary nor desirable. In this chapter plans are given for two excellent poultry houses which are provided with curtains which may be used to partly close the open fronts in cold storms. On many such houses the curtains are little used and often are abandoned as soon as they show signs of wear.

As a rule such curtains may comfort the house owner with the thot that he has provided additional protection for his fowls, but the fowls are sometimes handicapped rather than benefitted.

One of the very satisfactory features of the well-planned open-front house is that it is practically "fool proof," is very simple in construction and in operation and so requires but little attention. If curtains are provided to cover part of the open front, immediately the operator is confronted with the question, "How should the curtains be operated, should I leave them open or closed?" In a fickle climate like New England, especially close to the sea coast, the problem becomes big enough to be a nuisance. No one is sufficiently weather wise to be sure at all times what the weather may be between bedtime and sunrise. The poultryman may look for a cold, blowy or stormy night and close his curtains only to find that the night turned mild and the fowls would have been more comfortable with the house front entirely open. Again he may find, after keeping curtains closed for several nights, that the weather seems to give promise of continued mildness, only to arise in the morning and find deep snow upon the ground and the wind howling about the door, or it may be an ice storm which arrived unexpected and unannounced. The constant worry over and shifting of curtains is not only a nuisance but the frequent changes are not good for the fowls. They adapt themselves better to the open house conditions when the front always remains open. Where monitor windows are used if the day proves warm and sunny, the house temperature can be kept more uniform during the middle of the day by opening the monitor windows for an hour or so.

In the operation of my own houses, I seldom do much opening and closing of windows. The monitor windows are opened in early spring and remain that way until fall brings settled cold weather. In hot summer weather the other windows are left open. When cold weather comes the windows are all closed and remain so, as a rule. On the other hand, my birds have outdoor range most of the time and generally, except during severe winter storms, the house door is left wide open from the first feed in morning until fowls go to roost. If there is snow on the ground, an outdoor exercising space is cleared about the door. This means that there is plenty of air stirring thru the house between open front and the door. With the door closed and monitor windows open there is sufficient volume of fresh air circulating and the air movement on breezy days is less strenuous. It does not appear to make any difference to the fowls and it is more convenient for me to prop open the door when feeding and watering at breakfast time. However, let me say to the beginner, as did the old family doctor, "Don't do as I do, do as I advise"; so follow recommendations given for house operation in this and preceding chapters.

With experience in open-front housing of poultry will come confidence. It will be noted that the fowls are more comfortable and happy under natural open-air conditions and that their performance is better than under artificial ones. The open-front house provides protection plus comfort. The fowls can stand much more of open-air living and still do well, but for comfort, convenience and all around satisfactory results the well-built, well-managed, open-front house is best. When inclined to lack sufficient confidence to give the plan a fair trial, just remember the many small wild birds, also the quails, partridges, pheasants and other feathered friends that winter in our woods. I have close to fifty acres of woodland growing white pine and hard wood chiefly, some cedars, juniper, hemlock, and also a big grove of large white pine. Here, where the winter is bleak and cold, sudden temperature changes and storms frequent, our woods, especially where evergreens are abundant, are well tenanted with wild birds, large and small, all winter long. Besides the regulars many of the migratory birds stay with us thru the cold season. Robins and thrush make winter homes in the pines and junipers. The tiny titmouse is ever present and always has a cheery greeting as well as an acrobatic exhibition for those who visit the woodland.

The reader may have noted that I have made no provision for or recommendations concerning the artificial lighting of poultry houses to "lengthen the hen's day and increase egg production." I am inclined to look upon the plan as more or less of a fad, the value of which has been over-stated. In thickly populated centers where buildings are close together and where, because of cloudiness or smoke, the sky is often overcast the lighting plan may be a distinct advantage. But under open country conditions, as in the case of my own poultry, there is no occasion for lengthening the hen's day with artificial light. I get an abundant egg yield, equal to any I have seen reported by light faddists, I get it by natural methods and get a splendid yield during the short days of the year. In my own case it would not be good business judgment to go to the expense of installing and maintaining a house lighting system for the exclusive use of the fowls. Those who want lights can easily fit up open-front houses with them if desired.

A few words of caution here, restorative processes of the body take place mainly during sleep. To maintain health, keep resistance normal, build up the tissues of the body, make sure of elimination of waste and keep the whole body functioning properly, it is necessary to have activity and rest well balanced. More rest, particularly rest during sleep, is required during the period of short days and cold weather than during the period of mild and warm weather and longer days. It is easy to overdo the lengthening of the hen's day by means of artificial light.

In my own experience, when the days are shortening rapidly during November and thru the shortest days of December, my pullets are usually in full lay and the hens in their new plumage are beginning to increase egg production. The egg yield steadily gains, day by day, until it reaches maximum production in March and April. Now the longest days of the year come the latter part of June, but at this time egg production has begun to decline and there is a gradual slowing up all thru hot weather, tho the days are bright and long.

Fig. 43—The Gillette House, south front and east end view. See text.

Consider also prices obtainable in the wholesale egg market, which to a considerable extent reflects the state of supply and demand. Prices begin to climb in June and keep on going up until the peak prices are reached around Thanksgiving time. Soon after that feast day or early in December, sometimes the last of November, wholesale egg prices usually take a big drop. The pullets and the newly molted hens are beginning to make delivery in quantity. The prices keep on dropping until the bottom is reached in March and April. Now lights are put in use at the season when production is normally on the increase. I get a greater increase and better yield than most folks I know and get it by care and feeding, not by lights. Some other poultry keepers begin using egg-making tonics about the same season of increasing production. If they like to attribute their yield of eggs to artificial lighting or to use of stimulants, that is their affair, not mine, but I rather enjoy getting good results in a normal manner from healthy, vigorous birds that produce well and persistently because well fed and well cared for.

The Gillette House

The Gillette Open-Air House was designed by George K. Gillette, of Pembroke, Mass., when he was manager of Sugar Brook Poultry Farm, Central Village, Conn. I published the first plans of this house in March 1911 from sketches and photos made while visiting the farm. It is a good house adapted to the colony plan of poultry keeping.

The following fall a smaller colony house, 12x12 ft., arranged in two pens, was adapted from the Gillette plan and used to house the first North American International Laying Contest, Connecticut Agricultural College, Storrs, Conn. I was one of the members of the advisory board of this contest and intimately concerned with the matter

Fig. 44—Flock of White Plymouth Rocks enjoying corn stover litter by side of Gillette House. See text.

of houses and feeding formulas for contesting birds. This smaller house later became known as the Connecticut House, but it was and is essentially a modification of the Gillette House and was so specified at the time of adoption.

At the time of my visit the farm had eleven 20x20 ft. Gillette Open-Air Houses, each accommodating 150 White Plymouth Rock breeders and layers. The houses were in two rows located in a large fairly level field. The buildings were spaced about 50 feet apart in the row. Each was built on a concrete and stone foundation with floor well above ground level. Sand used on floor in place of litter. Litter of corn stover supplied out of doors between the houses. Altho the houses were fairly close together and the birds enjoyed free range the different flocks did not appear to mix to any great extent.

Fig. 43 is photographic view of south front and east end elevation of the Gillette house. With the plans given in this chapter the hen door at end, which hen is just leaving, is not necessary unless yards are provided at side of house as the lower half of the Dutch door is all that is required.

Fig. 44 shows a flock of White Rocks enjoying corn stover litter outside and between the colony houses.

Fig. 45 shows Gillette house front elevation (lower) and end section with frame detail (upper). In front elevation the open front is shown covered with wire screen. For this purpose I prefer one-quar-

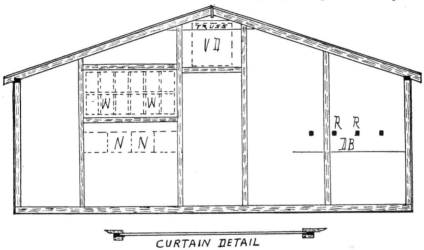

CURTAIN DETAIL

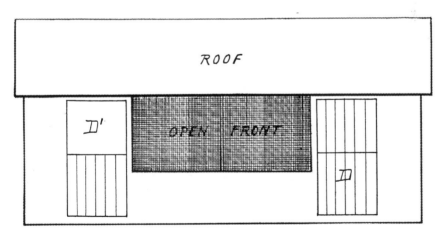

Fig. 45—Gillette House Plans. Lower shows front elevation, open front and Dutch doors. Top of left door (D') is open, right door (D) is closed. Upper plan shows east end section and frame plan. Sill is 20 ft. long. Front and rear studs each 6 ft. from top of sill to bottom of plate (plate shown in solid black). Studs either side of center 8 ft. 9 in. from top of sill to bottom of rafters. Windows (W), nests (N), ventilating door below peak (VD), roosts (R), dropping board (DB). See text.

ter-inch mesh galvanized wire netting, "square mesh cellar window wire cloth." There are two Dutch doors in front of house, doors divided horizontally in middle, upper and lower halves opening independently. Doors open in. Right hand door (D) is shown closed. Left door (D') is shown with upper half open. Upper figure shows frame detail of east end looking west. Windows (W) two half sash 6 light 8x12, are same in both ends. It is 4 ft. top of sill to bottom of stringer on which window rests. Nests (N) are shown below window, see also ground plan. The sills, studs and rafters are shown shaded. Truss from front to back rafter and board between rafters unshaded. Ventilating door (VD) at peak is same in both ends and used to keep house cool in hot weather. Roosts (R) about one foot above dropping

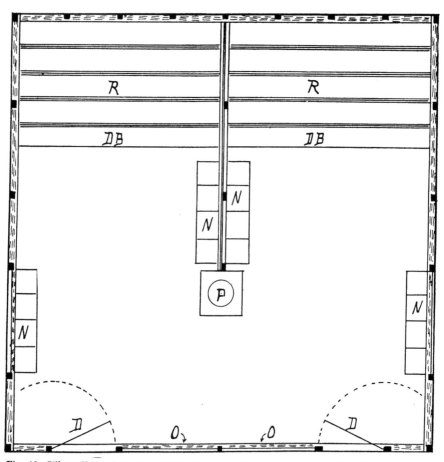

Fig. 46—Gillette House floor plan, 20x20. Location of studs shown in black. Middle partition from roof to floor extends from back wall to within 8 ft. of front. Doors (D) swing in as indicated by dotted lines. Nests (N), open front (O), raised platform and water fount (P), roosts (R), dropping board (DB). See text.

board (DB). Sills are 4x4s 20 ft. long. Corner studs are 2x4s, balance of studs, except in middle partition, 2x3s. Front and rear studs are 6 ft. high from top of sill to bottom of plate (shown in black at top of stud). Studs either side of center, 8 ft. 9 in. from top of sill to bottom of rafter. Rafters are 2x4s 11 ft. long and notched to fit plate.

Fig. 46 shows ground or floor plan 20x20 ft. Position of studs is shown in black on sills. This house has a middle partition from floor to roof extending from rear wall to within 8 ft. of the front. Studs are 2x4s and matched boards are used for partition. At end of partition is a platform, about 2 ft. square raised about 1 ft. above floor, on which drinking fountain (P) sits. Doors (D) open in as indicated by dotted lines. Open front (O). Nests (N) are about 2½ ft. above top of sill. Drop board (DB) about 2½ ft. above top of sill. Roosts (R) about one foot above drop board.

This 20x20 ft. colony house has overall dimensions 10 ft. high at peak of roof, 6 ft. 10 in. high at back and front. Built with matched or rabbeted board sides and ends, roof of matched boards covered with roofing fabric. Houses 100 to 150 fowls.

In Fig. 45 is shown curtain detail, see also Fig. 43. This coarse muslin curtain is built on a wood frame and made to slide up and down in cleats outside front of house to partly close the open front. The open front is 9 ft. wide by 3 ft. 9 in. high. The curtain, if used, should not close more than the lower 3 ft. of the open front at any time. Some use a similar curtain on the inside instead of outside of house, hung on hinges to swing in and up. It should never entirely close opening and should leave open space at top where protected by overhang of eaves. If I were building the house I would not provide a curtain. I believe the house would be better without it.

Lord Farms Leghorn House

Lord Farms, Methuen, Mass., specialize in heavy laying S. C. White Leghorns and baby chicks. They operate several farms, carry big breeding flocks, raise thousands of pullets and cockerels each season for breeding purposes, sell enormous quantities of hatching eggs and day old chicks. Such a business must have healthy, vigorous breeding stock or it cannot live.

They use open-front houses for breeding and growing stock on all the farms. Naturally, as the plant grew rapidly from a single farm to several farms, there are a number of different kinds of open-front buildings but all tend toward a particular fresh-air type.

I have taken what I consider two of the best types, the special 20x20 laying or breeding house and the dormer window breeding house and combined them in one. I believe it gives a colony type of building for large flock of Leghorns that is worthy to represent the Lord Farms type of open-front poultry house.

Fig. 47 shows the front elevation of this Lord Farms Leghorn House. The 20x20 laying house on farm has the same open front and windows at each side, but no dormer windows; while the dormer window house has the windows above front roof from which it takes the name and has the open front, but has no windows at sides of front. The left hand curtain (C1) is shown half way open. The middle curtain (C2) is wide open. The right hand curtain (C3) is shown closed, leaving small open space just below eaves. Each wire covered opening is 3 ft. high by about 4 ft. 8 in. wide. Fine mesh galvanized wire

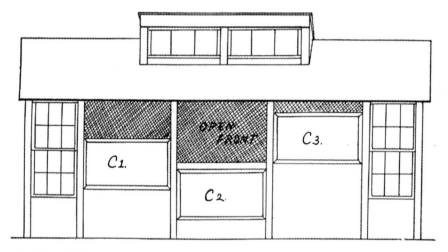

Fig. 47—Lord Farms Leghorn House. Front elevation. Curtain (C1) is shown half closed, middle curtain (C2) is wide open, right hand curtain (C3) is closed as much as it should ever be. Dormer windows are hung on transom swivels and open in at top and out at bottom. See text.

netting is used to protect front. The curtains slide in cleats, up and down on outside of front. Curtains are made about 4 ft. 8 in. wide by 2½ ft. high. The curtains used on houses at the farm close more of the open front and extend up until remaining opening is hidden by projection of overhang of front eaves. The curtains are used only in extremely severe winter weather and during storms. They can be adjusted at any height. House capacity 100 to 150 fowls.

While the winters in the neighborhood of Methuen are severe and driving snow, sleet and ice storms frequent enough to be decidedly disagreeable, I believe the curtain area given in plans herewith is ample for all purposes. On my own farm, with Woods houses, I have carried S. C. White Leghorns thru several severe winters with excellent results, no curtains of any sort used.

However, many of the houses at Lord Farms are on abrupt slopes, posted high in front to avoid necessity of expensive grading, some of them in very exposed locations, not all of them face so as to be protected from prevailing severe storms and some have nests below the open front. It was necessary to use the available land to best advantage. Under prevailing conditions the curtains undoubtedly prove a convenience.

Fig. 48 shows west end elevation and frame detail. The house is 20x20 floor plan, sets level on posts, has a matched board floor. The front and rear sills are 4x4s and are spiked to posts. End sills are formed by floor timbers, notched to fit front and rear sills and are 2x8s spaced 2 ft. apart by centers. A long 20 ft. brace sill 6x8, set on posts, supports floor timbers thru middle of house from end to end, see "B" in Fig. 48. Matched board floor is laid on floor timbers. Corner studs are 2x4s. Front corner studs extend from floor to bottom of upper plate and are 6 ft. long. Rear studs from floor to bottom of plate are 4 ft. long. Intermediate front studs extend from floor to bottom of plate below open front and from top of this plate to bot-

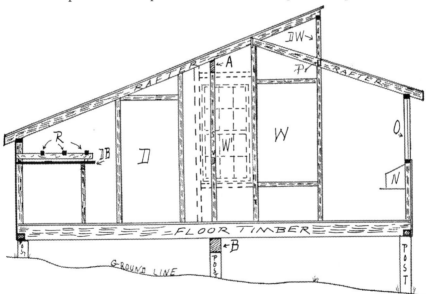

Fig. 48—Plan of Lord Farms House west end looking east showing frame detail. Floor timber is 20 ft. long notched to fit 4x4 sills at front and rear. Building sits level on posts to save grading expense on side hill. Front corner studs are 6 ft. from floor to bottom of top plate (in black). Rear studs are 4 ft. from floor to bottom of plate. From floor to top of board on which rafters butt is 9 ft. Truss of 2x8 (A) supplies added support to roof. Brace sill 6x8 (B) 20 ft. long runs under floor timbers. Dormer window (DW), dormer brace (P), open front (O), nests (N), west window (W), east window (W'), door in west end (D), roosts (R), drop board (DB). See text for further detail.

tom of upper plate; for these studs use 2x3s. Rafters are 2x4s spaced 2 ft. apart. Front rafters 9 ft. long, rear rafters 13½ ft. long, with extension rafter at dormer 3 ft. 9 in. long. Height of building over all at dormer, from bottom of floor timber to top of roof, about 11 ft. 4 in. The stud at this point is 7 ft. 7 in. from floor to bottom of rafter and 1 ft. 10 in. from top of rafter to bottom of dormer plate. Below the dormer window (DW) is a brace plate (P) between rafters.

Height of building at peak of roof, 9 ft. from floor to top of board on which front and rear rafters butt. Running from top of stud at west end over center stud in middle of house to brace above east window is a 2x8 truss (A) 20 ft. long to give added support to rear roof in heavy snow storms. Other detail in Fig. 48, door in west end (D),

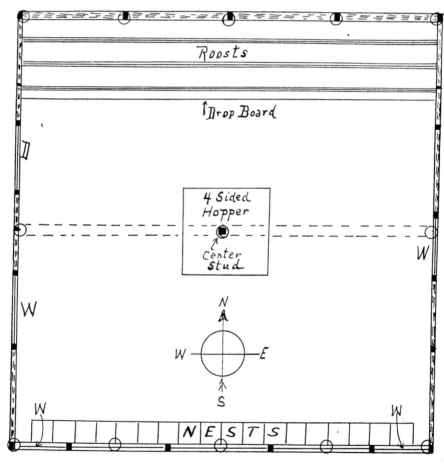

Fig. 49—Floor plan Lord Farms House, 20x20 ft. Dotted lines show location of brace sill under floor timbers. Small circles locate posts which support house. Door (D), windows (W). See text.

west window (W), east window (W') dotted lines, stud at side of east window in dotted lines, open front (O) ; roost platform or drop board (DB), 3 ft. above floor supported by posts and stringers, extends whole length of house. Roosts (R) about 5 inches above drop board. Nests, with slant roof to keep clean and dry, (N) extend length of house just below open front.

Fig. 49 is floor plan. Circles on sills and floor timber indicate position of cedar posts which support house. Door (D), windows (W). Nests may or may not project behind windows at either side of front as shown. Dotted lines show position of 6x8 brace sill (B) below floor timbers. The center stud is a 4x4 and supports truss (A). Around center stud at convenient height from floor is built a 4-sided feed hopper. Water pans can be located under corners of hopper.

These plans are drawn to scale. Take the known sill or floor timber length, 20 ft., halve it and divide the half into ten equal parts, these represent feet ; divide one foot into 12 equal parts and you have inches. This gives a scale sufficiently accurate for purpose of getting dimensions of any part of the plan.

The dormer windows are cellar window sash, the end windows are single sash 12 lights, such as used for double windows. These windows are hung on swivel hangers midway between top and bottom, like a door transom, and equipped with transom rods, so that windows open in at top and out at bottom.

Overall height dimensions of this house from bottom of sill to top of roof are, front 7 ft. 4 in. ; rear 5 ft. 4 in. ; at dormer window stud 11 ft. 4 in. ; at peak or junction of front and rear roof 9 ft. 10 in.

The Stoddard Southern House

The late H. H. Stoddard, pioneer poultry editor and poultry journal publisher of the early 'Seventies, was a friend of mine and a valued correspondent for many years. "Old Timers" will remember how eagerly they looked for the arrival of Stoddard's American Poultry Yard (weekly) and Poultry World (monthly).

Mr. Stoddard was a close student of poultry husbandry ; from the early days a fresh air advocate and in later years an ardent booster for the open-front house and fresh-air methods.

When he was well advanced in years, some time after the age when many men feel entitled to retire from the active list, Mr. Stoddard, with his family, went pioneering into "new country" in Texas and established a poultry farm there. He had many interesting experiences about which he wrote at length and he made himself familiar with the means of solving some of the problems with which poul-

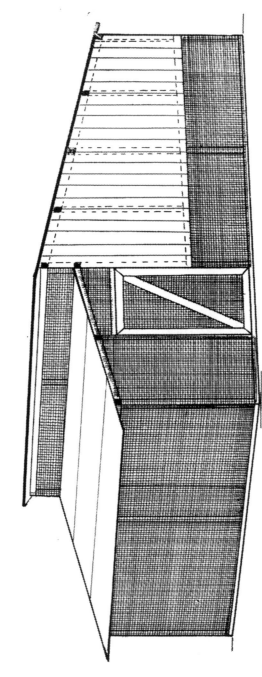

Fig. 50—The Stoddard Southern House, 10x16 ft., front and east side elevation. Overall dimensions 6 ft. 7 in. high at front and rear, 9 ft. 7 in. at monitor top. House mainly enclosed in fine mesh wire netting except a part of sides and back which are matched boards as indicated. Studs are shown in outline in wired parts and in dotted lines on boards. Horizontal rafters are located in solid black. House has concrete floor and foundation and is bolted to same. House capacity 40 fowls. See text.

try keepers in warm or hot climates are confronted. He tried keeping poultry in fenced enclosures with roosts unprotected in the open, tried roosts under roofed shelters and in wire cages, and had good results with all.

In his letters he gave me much data concerning poultry keeping in the south and made suggestions concerning housing problems and securing freedom from insect pests. Here in the north we find lice and mites sufficiently troublesome, but we do not have the ticks, the big chicken bugs, stick-tight fleas, and similar pests that make life a burden for both poultry and poultry keeper in some parts of the sunny southland.

The Stoddard Southern House, illustrated and described herein, was not designed by Mr. Stoddard. It is simply my attempt to embody in practical form some of the many good suggestions he made.

Most of the insect pests affecting poultry hide in dark places, in cracks and crannies of the building, or in shady or dark places in moist earth and sand, and there breed and multiply. Like other evil doers they pursue their wicked trade under cover of the darkness and shun bright light. Obviously the less furnishings and the more light in the southern poultry house the better.

In a warm climate, even tho the nights are cool and sometimes frost comes in winter, a poultry house is chiefly of value to confine the fowls, furnish some protection against thieves, furred, feathered and human—I put the human hen thief last because he belongs to a very low order of animal life—and afford shelter from storms and hot sun. It needs to be built to keep cool rather than for warmth.

The Stoddard Southern House is built with a foundation and floor of concrete. The sills are 2x4s, placed 4 inch side up, thoroly treated with creosote and bolted to the concrete foundation to protect the house from high winds. The floor dimensions are 10 ft. wide by 16 ft. deep. No floor plan is needed.

Figure 50 shows east side and front elevation of the house. It will be noted that the greater part of the house is fine mesh wire netting (galvanized of course). Location of door is shown. A poultry door can be added if desired. Position of studs is indicated in outline behind wire and in dotted lines on boarded in section. Corner studs are 2x4s, others 2x3s. Rafters are 2x4s and are placed horizontally, 2 in. side up, on top of studs. These rafters are indicated in black in Fig. 50. Roof boards are put on up and down, or at right angles to rafters. Galvanized or rust proof metal shingles would be excellent for covering roof, or use gray asbestos shingles.

The front and rear rafters of each roof serve in place of plates.

Front and rear studs from top of sill to bottom of rafter are each 6 ft. Stud for half-monitor is placed 10 ft. from rear wall. This stud is a 2x4 and is 9 ft. from top of sill to bottom of upper rafter. Rear rafter of front roof is about 15 in. below upper rafter and is braced into studs at sides. The opening in monitor is about 14 in. high by width of the house and is covered with fine mesh galvanized wire netting only.

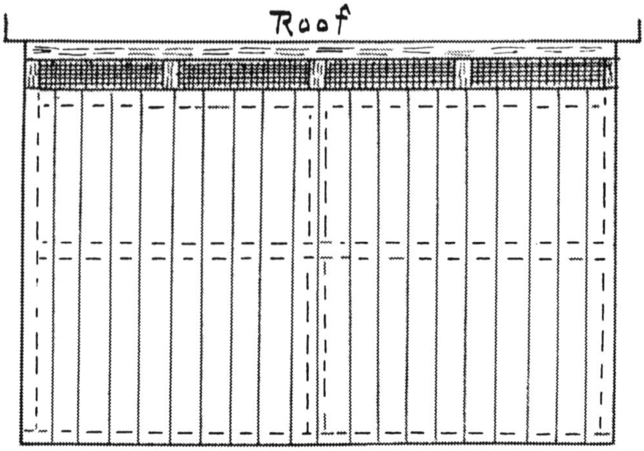

Fig. 51—Rear wall elevation of Stoddard Southern House. Wired in part below horizontal rafter is 6 in. high by width of house, balance of rear wall is matched boards as indicated. Sill, studs and stringers shown in dotted lines. See text.

Fig. 51 shows rear wall of house. Dotted lines indicate sill, studs and stringers. Rear rafter and short studs supporting same are shown shaded. The opening, covered with wire netting, just below horizontal rafter is 6 in. high by width of house. This, with opening in half monitor, aids in keeping house from becoming too hot and insures good circulation of air directly under roof. Below this rear opening the house wall is boarded with matched boards put on up and down as shown and closing rear wall from bottom of opening to base of sill.

As will be noted in Fig. 50 the side walls are wire netting to a distance of 2½ ft. above top of sill in high rear section. The balance of this rear section is covered in with matched boards. Sides and front of lower front part of house are made of wire netting.

Wire nests, obtainable of any poultry supply concern, are hung about the sides of the house where convenient. They should be hung on screw hooks so as to be quickly detachable and easily removed for kerosening and cleaning.

The roosts are placed on two carpenter's horses. These horses should be made with a piece of 4x4 for a body and four legs well braced quite wide apart. Lower part of body of horse should be about 3 ft. from floor. Each horse carries three spikes driven into it on top side and spaced 18 inches apart. These spikes engage and hold the roosts. Fig. 52 shows outline of horse side view and end view. Spike (S) is shown at left. Roost (R) is shown in center. Spike solid line above horse and dotted in same, and roost dotted (RS).

The three roosts are each 8 ft. long and made of 2x3s placed 3 in. side up. Roosts are drilled at each end, about 8 in. from end in center, to engage spike. Roosts should fit spikes snugly and at same time be easily removed. Place horses supporting roosts in rear section of house well away from side walls and about 2 ft. from rear wall. Here fowls will be amply protected from wind and storm and will find comfortable sleeping quarters. Roosts and horses should be painted with creosote and thoroly dried before using. Remove from house frequently—once a week—kerosene them freely and dry in sun. No drop-

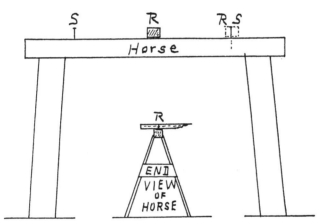

Fig. 52—Roost detail for Stoddard Southern House. Outline is shown of 4-legged wooden horse, body piece of 4x4. End view also shown. Lower part of horse body 3 ft. from floor. Roosts fit on spikes and are quickly detached. Two horses used. Detail: Spike (S) shown without roost. Roost (R) drilled to fit in place over spike. Spike in solid black above top of horse and dotted where driven into 4x4, roost outline in dotted lines (RS). Spikes are 18 in. apart. Roosts are 2x3s 8 ft. long and drilled for spikes at 8 in. from each end. See text.

ping board is used. Sweep up droppings from beneath roosts often.

Overall dimensions of this house are 10x16 floor plan, 6 ft. 7 in. high front and rear, 9 ft. 7 in. high at monitor.

It is a good plan to give woodwork of outside of house, and studding in wire enclosed parts, a good coat of green or brown creosote shingle stain. Interior of house including roof should be painted white with some good disinfecting white paint. Some of the water paints are excellent and cheap enough to use often. Paint the interior white and keep it white. If walls and under side of roof are painted with white oil paint, whole house can be washed out regularly with the aid of a hose or bucket spray pump. Keep it clean and free from accumulations of dirt and dust. The white interior will add to the light in enclosed section. With plenty of light and air, reasonable cleanliness observed, the house should be practically free from dangerous insect pests.

If turkey gnats and mosquitoes are very troublesome, use fine galvanized mosquito netting to enclose wire parts of house. Keep large door closed and provide a small hen door covered with a slit curtain of burlap which has been moistened with kerosene. When a gnat invasion is expected, spray wire netting with kerosene daily until danger is past. If a number of the pests invade the interior of house, make a smudge with pyrethrum (Persian insect powder) burned on a shovelful of hot coals, inside house to clear it of the gnats and mosquitoes. Fly killer sprays may prove useful.

The house should prove very comfortable quarters for fowls in warm climates. How should the house face? That is a question that each builder will have to decide to meet conditions in his location. Here in the north I build my open-front houses to face south or south by east. This gives ample sunlight in interior. The prevailing severe storms here are from the northeast and southwest, the storms that carry rain and snow and a slant of high wind that is almost horizontal. A windbreak of pine woods protects us on northwest. With the house so placed the bad storms strike it on the quarter, at a slant on side and end, so that the force of the wind is deflected. I would place the southern house so that sunlight in early morning and late afternoon will penetrate most of interior and ample shade be given during the hot part of day. The prevailing severe storms should strike the house at a slant on side and rear walls to turn aside as much as possible the force of wind. The location should be well drained both as to air and water drainage. The concrete floor should be high enough above ground level to keep it reasonably dry and permit it to dry quickly after heavy rains.

CHAPTER VIII

Discussion and Testimony Concerning Woods Open-Front Houses—Air Circulation—The Wrong and the Right Way to Build—Brooding Equipment— Small Size Woods House for Small Flocks and for Brooder

"Every great movement must experience three stages: ridicule, discussion, adoption."—John Stuart Mills.

THAT the fresh-air movement, promoting better living conditions both day and night for man, beast and fowl, is a great movement no one can successfully deny. Living under practically open-air conditions has worked miracles.

Tho widely adopted, open-front poultry houses are still the subject of much discussion, particularly by those who, like the merchant, have "something just as good" of their own brand to offer, and there are a few die-hard opponents who attempt ridicule.

H. H. Stoddard in 1914 said:— "I believe that in time over a wide belt of country the invaluable open front will be on two or three sides of the roosting room instead of one only, in which case tight doors can be arranged to cover, occasionally the two extra open sides if these happen to be to the windward in stress of weather.

"Regarding the thousands of open-front poultry houses Dr. Woods has given this country, which affords an ocean of fresh air, wide as heaven and deep as the other place, to the myriads of pairs of lungs hungry for it, there is another sanitary boon he has bestowed in the shape of temporary summer roosts in groves, with no shelter except the green boughs. This practice, I am sure, will spread, especially as it is well in line with the 'back-to-nature' slogan so popular these days in other matters."

From letters received I learn that in some quarters, frequently among those who do their poultry work by proxy and confine themselves to poultry keeping on paper and talking about it to audiences of various sizes, there is more or less criticism unfavorable to all open-front houses and to the Woods house in particular. I would not discuss this matter further, but for the ever-increasing army of beginners who do not understand, and who take a good deal of what they read and hear as gospel without weighing the evidence.

I have been breeding and rearing poultry since boyhood. My poultry experience began back in the 'Seventies and it has continued almost without a break since that time. For the past 29 years I have been writing about poultry and conducting experimental work with poultry. Most of that time I have had good sized flocks of popular breeds and have done the work myself, including the drudgery. I want my information first hand, not by proxy or hearsay. Except on several occasions when I have been managing and growing several thousand head of poultry and had to have help, my poultry work and observations have been personally conducted.

What I know about open-front houses has been learned thru building them, using them under different conditions, and observing the work of others who have used them. I am in and out of my own poultry houses daily and I have often studied conditions in these houses by lantern-light on cold winter nights.

Poultry Club Members and Community Poultry House, Middletown, Va.
(Courtesy of the U. S. Department of Agriculture.)

I would like to see every poultry keeper use some type of good open-front house. Of course I am pleased when they prefer my type, but the thing that interests me chiefly in this matter is that open-front poultry houses be used more and more to the improvement of poultry health, production of better poultry, and greater comfort for the fowls.

Every semi-monitor house is not necessarily a Woods house. Half-monitor houses of the closed type were used long before I was born. When I planned the Woods type of house I made a choice of certain desirable dimensions, made a few improvements in construction, took out partitions, made a different arrangement of windows and furnishings, and **opened the front.** There are three essential features of the Woods house besides the open front: (a) a high rear section and low front section with unobstructed floor space from back wall to open front; (b) a deep house from front to back, square in case of 20x20 house, much deeper than wide in case of 10x16 and smaller sizes; (c) greater depth to the high rear section than the low front section, the peak of monitor usually being over a point on the scratching floor about midway between edge of front roost (or front of dropping board if there is one) and the wire front. The door and windows are so placed that drafts cannot disturb fowls on the roosts. With this construction there need be no fear of "trapping" the warm moist air back of monitor windows, which seems to worry some theorists.

More About Dampness

During the big blizzard of early January I received this letter, which is only one of many like it:

"Dear Doctor: We expect to build quite a number of houses and are in doubt what to put up. Your house has always appealed but, as

On author's farm after January blizzard. Tolman house at left, Woods house, 10x16, at right.

you no doubt know, Prof. ——— says it is a failure in some locations. He says that the moisture caused by heat rising from fowls condenses on upper windows and that it is necessary to remove half the sash and replace with screen.

All our present houses are so-called fool proof type, but we are having our troubles with them. One that by all the laws of Nature should be damp is the driest, and one that should be dry is almost wet. Am unable to account for cause.   A. M."

Dampness in poultry houses has been a vexing problem for a long time, probably since the first poultry houses were built. It gives far less trouble in an open-front house than in a closed house. Frequently it is due to crowding the house beyond its capacity. Fowls do not sweat, they lose very little heat thru the skin because the feathers are almost perfect insulation. The urine of fowls contains very little moisture. The fowl gets rid of excess moisture and body heat thru the exhaled breath. If this moisture-laden exhaled air has an opportunity to condense on cold ceiling, walls or windows, instead of being carried off by good circulation of fresh-air thru an open front, it may be seen as dampness or frost. In the case of poorly constructed, badly located and closed houses the amount of such moisture may be excessive. Poorly built concrete floors may be damp. The location may be damp and the air drainage poor. Deep litter allowed to remain in house overlong may collect and hold dampness. Frequent sudden changes in temperature during winter, fogs, long rain storms, alternating snow and rain, may so load the air with moisture that some of it is bound to condense on house walls and even on metalwork of automobiles and machinery kept in tight unheated buildings. One has to use his common sense and reasoning powers in dealing with this matter.

On page 923, June 1914, American Poultry Journal is a report of a visit to the Missouri State Poultry Experiment Station, which contains the following:

"Mr. Quisenberry told us that the two houses of the Woods type and the Missouri Station Farmer's Fool-proof Poultry House, all with cement floors, were the only houses where it had been possible to keep the litter material dry enough to burn when removed at cleaning time."

This report received the written endorsement of Mr. Quisenberry after it was published.

I consider my home farm a very damp location in winter. We are on the shore of a pond and large lake, about three miles from the ocean, and there are many lakes and ponds all around us. Water is very near the surface of the soil, we can find a spring almost anywhere within 4 to 12 feet of surface.

All thru the latter part of December (1922) we had heavy fogs, some snow and considerable rain. The first twelve days of January were "just one darn storm after another," rain, ice storms, high winds, snow in blizzard proportions, more rain and ice, frequent extreme changes in temperature occurring suddenly. Such weather conditions are difficult and severely test any house. Our fowls in Woods houses were happy and comfortable all thru the period, egg production kept steadily increasing. Some parts of the houses were a bit too dusty. There was a little frost at times on the monitor and side windows when I opened up for morning feeding, but not so much as was to be seen on the windows of our residence where three big wood stoves are going day and night. There was no dampness of any importance in these houses. Such litter as there was in use was dry enough to burn. The nests were dry. There was dust all thru the house. I would not call that a damp poultry house and do not believe that any-one else honestly considers it so.

Air Circulation in Woods Houses

The semi-monitor type of open-front houses has been used under all sorts of conditions, made friends in widely different climates and been praised by competent construction engineers who know what good ventilation is. It provides for good distribution of fresh-air thruout the house at all times, without drafts and without undesir-able dampness. No one wants or expects absolutely dry air. Air of desert dryness is not comfortable. No one could or should expect any house to change the character of the out-door air.

Author's Farm. Portable 10x16 Woods house used as brooder. Cheese cloth curtain shown at left was discarded after first season and no curtains used.

Often in winter when there is bare ground I open the doors of the houses and let the fowls run free. Sometimes I make a poor guess concerning the weather and a sudden northeast gale springs up bring-ing with it cold rain or snow. The east doors are open. The fowls are all over the place and beyond the ditches in a big hayfield across the road. Rain drives in at the open door and makes a comparatively small but very wet place on the floor between door and open front. The hens finally decide to come home pretty well drenched. They do not appear to mind it. I may have been called away and house remains open most of day. When fowls are finally shut in house they are wet and part of house floor is very wet. This happens frequently. Yet, the house dries out surprisingly quick, the fowls are always dry and in fine fettle within a short time after they are shut in. Sometimes in driving storms a house roof springs a leak. The house always dries out quickly. The fowls do not suffer any inconvenience and keep in perfect health. Such conditions would not prevail in a closed type house and could not happen if the house were really damp.

Thru many seasons I have carefully tested the circulation of air in Woods houses under different conditions, in calm weather, in driving rain and snow storms, and great gales, with the house empty, and with fowls working in litter, or at night with them at rest on the roost. Smoke was used to test the air currents in various parts of house. During storms the average extreme penetration of the wind was tested, marking the point where it could be felt upon face or moistened finger. Always the actual penetration of either snow or rain was very much less, seldom more than a few inches back of the wire. In Fig. 53, the upper diagram shows end elevation of house and average path of circulation of air indicated by arrows. It will be noted that the cold out-door air enters all along the open front except close up near roof, that it is deflected toward the floor and curves upward just past center of house. If no dropping board is used, it flows up above the roosts, curves toward the monitor and down under the low front roof passing out at top of open front. There are variations due to outside conditions and movement of fowls or attendant in the house, but the air current is fairly constant as shown. Where a dropping board is used the direction of air current is about the same except that the exchange of air under the board is slower, but by day is kept agitated by fowls constantly running in and out. Dropping board and air current below, shown in dotted lines. Of course, when monitor windows are opened there is a strong air current up and out thru these windows. This is not a draft. (See discussion of drafts in Chapter I).

The "Air Cushion"

James B. Morman, of Maryland, discussing the Woods house says:

"This type of house has been used in the extremely cold and windy climate of British Columbia, Canada. In describing the use of open-front poultry houses of the Woods type for severely cold climates, the report of the Department of Agriculture for that province for 1909 says:

" 'The birds are protected at all times from drafts by the tight back, sides and roof. Only one side of the house being open, cold winds do not penetrate the house. The fowls are more comfortable all of the time and seem to enjoy the greater abundance of fresh air than is supplied by the old closed house or when the air is diffused thru a curtain.'

"Now, what is the explanation of this phenomenon? There are two principal reasons for it: (1) Because the over-hanging eaves and wire front serve as a partial protection against wind and rain storms; and (2) because the atmosphere on the inside of the room or building acts as an air cushion which the pressure of the outlying atmosphere can only overcome to a limited extent: * * * * *

"On a breezy day, stand in an open window of a room otherwise closed, and the pressure of the outside atmosphere will be felt with ease. Then insert into the window an ordinary wire mosquito screen,

Summer view of one of 20x20 Woods' houses in an oak grove, author's farm, with flock of young White Plymouth Rocks.

and the entrance of outside atmosphere can be scarcely felt. The wire screen not only prevents the free entrance of the outlying atmosphere, but the partially confined atmosphere on the inside acts as a resisting body or an air cushion."

Dr. W. C. Dumble, Toronto, Ont., expressing appreciation of Mr. Morman's report concerning the Woods house, said:

"The underlying principles of the air cushion and the circulation of air inward and upward and outward, produced by the method of construction of surfaces and natural heat of the fowls, appeal as correct to any hen lover with ordinary horse sense. The air cushion idea, I believe, is a fact of immense importance and ought to revolutionize the house building methods and thru that the whole poultry industry. * * * * *

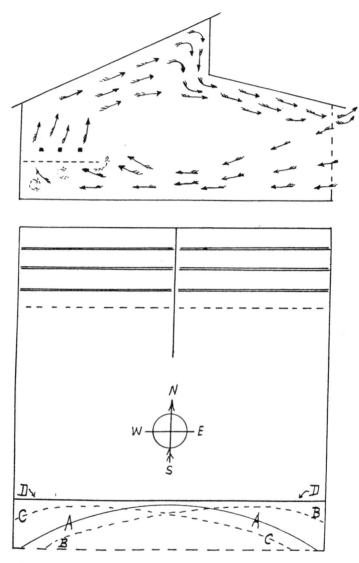

Fig. 53—Circulation of air in Woods open-front houses. Arrows in upper figure show direction of air currents diffusing air from open front when house is empty or when fowls are on roost. With fowls actively at work there are, of course, many variations, but general course of the ventilating current is fairly constant. Lower figure shows outline of 20x20 house floor plan. Solid line "A,A" is so-called "air-cushion" or point of extreme penetration of strong wind from the south. Dotted line "B,B" shows average extreme penetration of severe storms from the southwest. Dotted line "C,C" shows average extreme penetration of strong gales from southeast. Extreme penetration is point where wind can only be detected by face or moistened finger. Rain or snow seldom penetrates beyond a few inches back of wire front. "D,D" indicates a 10-inch litter board, held in cleats, used by some to keep litter away from open front. It is 3 ft. back from wire and space between wire front and litter board is covered with a few inches of sand or earth to serve as a dusting place. See text.

"It is somewhat remarkable that so many prominent poultry writers still appear to regard old style houses as suited to the business. However it always takes time for truth to displace error, but there is no doubt many new buildings will adopt the monitor and extended front."

J. R. Little, Illinois, says, "Next to the open front, I consider the prime feature of efficiency in this style of house to be its depth from front to back."

The outline of ground plan of Woods house in Fig. 53 shows the average curve of the so-called "air cushion," under various conditions of severe winds and driving snow and rain. The test house faced almost due south and was in an exposed location. The solid line "A" indicates the average extreme penetration of a severe storm from the south. Dotted line "B" shows the average curve of extreme penetration in a driving storm from the southwest. Dotted line "C" shows similar curve for southeast storm. This line of extreme penetration only marks the point at which the wind could be detected by the face of observer or his moistened finger. The actual penetration of rain or snow thru the wire front was very much less, seldom more than a few inches.

The straight solid line "D" indicates a ten inch "litter board" recommended by some users. The board is placed on edge about three feet back from the wire front. Straw or other litter is kept back of this board. Between the "litter board" and the wire front, a few inches of fine sand or earth are kept on the floor and this makes a good dusting place for the fowls. I do not use the litter board except for young chicks.

Economical Construction

Robert Topping, Tennessee, writing of the Woods house in 1916 says, "I noticed your article dealt only with the use of the house in the colder climates, but I have found that this type of house does wonderfully well and can be used in a variety of ways in our southern climate.

"In my opinion the monitor type of house has several advantages. The construction of it is more economical than most houses, as you get the same floor space with about two-thirds as much wall space. Its adaptability also appeals to me. I have used it for an incubator house, a brooder house, for young stock on the range, and for housing breeders both summer and winter, and it has given the best of service for all uses. Birds in a house of this type are really, as you say, always healthy and cheerful in any kind of weather."

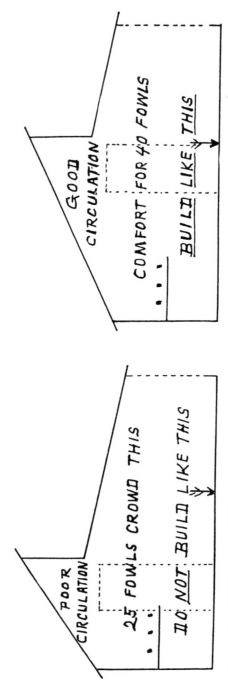

Fig. 54—The WRONG and the RIGHT way to build a Woods open front house. Both are semi-monitor open fronts. The one at LEFT has smaller capacity, does not get enough light, sun and air, is drafty and unsatisfactory. The house at the RIGHT has correct proportions for a Woods house, a comfortable, cheerful home for fowls and gets abundant fresh air, light and sunshine. Arrow indicates center of scratching floor. See text.

The Wrong and the Right Way

Some builders get the rear part of the semi-monitor house much too shallow. That explains nine-tenths of the cases reporting trouble. Some do not build house high enough.

Fig. 54 shows in outline two 10x16 houses. Both are semi-monitors. The one at the **left** is built **wrongly,** it has not the proper proportions of a Woods house. The rear part is too shallow. This roosting section has smaller capacity and **25 fowls will crowd it.** The circulation of air is poor. The monitor windows, in so shallow a rear part, are of little service except as ventilators when open. Warm moist air may be "trapped" in this shallow monitor section. The peak of monitor is too far to the rear of scratching floor center (see arrow). This wrongly built house does not get enough light, sunshine, and fresh air. Roosts may be drafty at night from cracks around badly located door (see dotted lines.) The house at the **right** is a Woods open-front house and is **well proportioned.** It is built **properly.** The rear section has greater depth than the low front section. There is ample cubic foot air capacity in this roosting section, **comfortable quarters for 40 fowls.** Light, sunshine and fresh air in abundance may penetrate all parts of house. The air circulation is good at all times and there are no drafts. Warm moist air does not "trap" in the monitor. Peak of monitor is almost directly above the center of scratching floor (see arrow). Be sure to **build** your semi-monitor poultry house **properly.**

In 1917, A. F. Marzian, Indiana, wrote:

"The trouble with most of the anti-fresh-air folks is that not one has given the open-front poultry house a thoro trial under proper conditions. Most of them try to go the inventor one better, by adding here and taking off there. They are always experimenting and invariably fail.

"I have a 10x16 open-front house built exactly according to Dr. Woods' plans. Never had a sick bird. Not even a sign of a cold in the entire flock of 40 pullets. Am getting a 60 to 70 per cent egg production. Ten above zero in Indiana is far more disagreeable than 10 below in the northern states. And I know what I am talking about. Was raised in a country where we had seven months of snow out of the twelve, and 'got so cold the thermometer got the pneumonia' as Billy Golden expresses it.

"I wish some of the anti-fresh-air people could hear the daily concert in my open-front house, as rendered by my White Plymouth Rocks. My, how they sing and cackle and talk! They make the 'welkin ring' for sheer joy of living!"

John A. Gamewell, New Jersey, Hamburg fancier, in 1917, said:

"I tried several other styles of coops until finally I saw a cut of what has become known as the Woods open-front type, and I immediately decided that this was the style of house that I wanted. I obtained plans and had several of them built. This style of house I have adopted to the exclusion of any other. I found that my birds did splendidly in them, even in the coldest weather. Some people seem to think that the Golden Penciled Hamburgs are not a very hardy variety, but I can assure you that all of my birds are raised and kept in this type of house, and the results are very gratifying. * * * * * I believe that if an arrangement could be made whereby fowls could be exhibited in open-air houses, the results would be much more beneficial, and our exhibition stock would not be subjected to these different diseases. Pure fresh air is the best tonic I know of for the successful raising of all varieties of fowls."

Not a Cold House

The semi-monitor type house is not a cold house as compared with some other open-front houses and closed types. It is far more comfortable in cold weather than any closed house. Even with varieties having large single combs there is much less trouble with frostbitten combs and wattles in the Woods house than in the usual type of closed building.

Of course getting combs and wattles "nipped" by frost is not altogether a matter of housing. The bird's condition at the time has a great deal to do with it. The comb is more apt to freeze when exposed to cold wind, as a rule, than when the bird is on the roost at night. The sleeping bird usually tucks its head under its wing. Wattles are usually frostbitten after getting them wet in drinking water. That is one reason why some folks prefer to use snow in place of water in extreme cold weather. Sudden extreme temperature changes, with a quick drop from mild weather to below zero temperatures, are favorable to producing frostbite. I have known S. C. White Leghorns in an open-front house to escape frostbite, when on the same night in a closed house on an adjoining farm a Cochin had comb, wattles and toes frozen badly. A friend of mine received a Minorca cockerel during mild winter weather. As the mercury was dropping rapidly that evening, he put the bird in its shipping coop in the loft over the cow barn, thinking to protect it from having comb frozen. It would have been much better to have put the bird into the poultry house. As it happened, the temperature fell sharply to below zero and the bird lost its comb and wattles from frostbite. Lack of resisting power and close confinement in bad air under low temperatures is the explanation.

J. R. Galloway, Indiana, in 1917 writing about a flock of W. F. Black Spanish housed in a Woods open-front building, reported good egg yield and said, "I have never had colds or roup in my flocks since using the open-front house."

Geo. M. Rounds, Alberta, Canada, reporting for a flock of exhibition S. C. White Leghorns wintered in a Woods house by William McKenzie, a fancier in Claresholm, wrote:

"It seemed to me that a Woods house with S. C. White Leghorns in such a climate as this would get about its supreme test. Mr. McKenzie thot I was crazy when I first talked to him. There were no closed houses here but what sent out frozen combs every winter. If a tight house did that, what magic could keep combs from freezing in an open-front house? * * * * * He agreed to change over one of his houses to the Woods plan. This house has been in operation a little over a year, (fall of 1915).

"Last winter the mercury did not go over 30 degrees below zero here, however the closed houses gave forth their frozen combs as usual. For the first time in Mr. McKenzie's long experience with poultry there was **not a comb frozen** or touched among the birds living in the Woods plan house. One night only, and there were several colder nights later, Mr. McKenzie put a blanket over the screened front. You can more readily appreciate his temptation on that night when I tell you that the birds in that house were his choicest ones and later made almost a clean sweep of the biggest shows in this province.

"To use Mr. McKenzie's own words, this Woods house put an end to the frozen comb problem and his winter egg yield was much larger than usual. There was absolutely no sickness and his birds were not only in fine physical condition but they seemed to have an unusual amount of energy."

J. W. Dunfield, writing from Kingsbury, Quebec, in 1914, said:

"We have had about the coldest winter on record here and of the ten Woods open-front poultry houses in the neighborhood I have heard nothing but good.

"I see that you advocate no dropping boards in the Woods house. I did not find this plan satisfactory in this bleak climate where it is very cold and stormy. The hens seemed to be colder when there were no dropping boards and they would roost on the nest platforms. As soon as I put in dropping boards I had no further trouble."

B. L. Billings, Vermont, was an early user of Woods house. In 1914 he reported fine egg yield and that he had never had sickness nor trouble with Rhode Island Reds housed in these open-front buildings. Writing about extreme weather conditions he said:

"Two years ago we had winter weather when the mercury dropped to 38 degrees below zero, and this year it has been down to 35 degrees below, and was 25 degrees below zero yesterday morning (January 23, 1914) and today it is raining; so you see it is quite a stunt to take care of 80 degrees variation in temperature in so short a time. The Woods house proved such a success that I built another last fall."

Robert G. Bailey, in Western Poultry for January 1919, writing of the Woods house said:

"About the first of the year Lewiston (Idaho) experienced a decided cold spell, and in some portions of the district the thermometer registered around the zero mark. The editor of this magazine is using an open-front semi-monitor house and there was not a frosted comb or wattle to be found after the passing cold spell, even tho this house was in a place where the thermometer registered as low as any place in the valley. I have visited several places more favorably located and frozen combs are the invariable rule. Yes, it costs more to construct a real poultry house than it does a shed, but there are so many advantages that the progressive poultrymen should take heed and help themselves to make progress.

"The modern house I refer to is entirely open on the front and never has a curtain of any kind been used. The fowls are happy and contented all winter, and no matter how severe the weather, seem not to be affected in the least in egg yield. Even tho at times the thermometer has gone to several degrees below zero, with but one exception, I have not had a frosted comb in three years."

I might go on and fill many more pages with testimony as to the value and desirability of the semi-monitor open-front house, but the few reports given in this chapter ought to hold the critics and knockers for a while.

The Woods House as a Brooder House

The Woods type house has been successfully used as a brooder house with coal burning brooder stoves, oil burning canopy hovers, and outdoor brooders of the "Wigwarm" type. For this purpose the house has been used with and without curtains. I prefer to do without curtains. If a curtain is used it should be made of cheese cloth on light wooden frame and hinged at the top, back of the open front, to swing in and hook up to rafters. If muslin (cotton cloth) is used for curtain, it should not cover upper six inches of the open-front. I have not used curtains, when using house to brood chicks after first trial. One of my friends used a 10x16 with a coal burning brooder stove and tried muslin curtains. He found that he had to open monitor windows a little in order to have stove run well when curtains were closed. The muslin or cotton cloth does not allow air to pass freely enough. Cheese cloth seems to satisfy the requirements of those who want curtains.

Using the 10x16 house without curtains and with a coal burning brooder stove, one farmer raised to market age 900 chicks out of

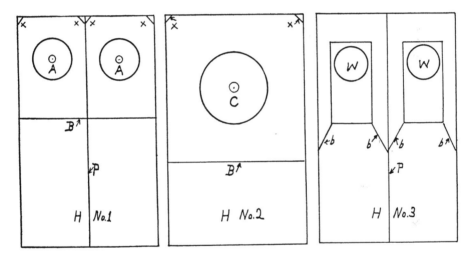

Fig. 55—Plans for use of coal or oil burning canopy brooders and "out-door" brooders in 10x16 size Woods houses. House No. 1 has two medium size canopy brooders (A,A), movable partition board (B), partition board from front to back (use 10 or 12 in. board) (P), Corner blocks (X). House No. 2 has large canopy brooder (C), for heating with oil or coal. House No. 3 has two "Wigwarm" type out-door brooders, with hot water and hot air hovers (W,W), lamp heated. Partition board (P). Corner boards to keep chicks in front of brooder (b,b). See text.

1000 chicks put under a 1200-chick-capacity hover. Part of chicks were taken by hawks and a cat. Another did equally well with an oil burning canopy hover of big capacity. I should prefer smaller flocks and would not try to brood more than half the chicks named in manufacturer's capacity rating. For the 1000 to 1200 chick-capacity brooder I consider a flock of 500 plenty big enough.

Where the house is to be used for brooding chicks it must have a floor, preferably well-constructed concrete altho matched boards will serve. If a coal burning brooder stove is used it will be necessary to run galvanized chimney thru the roof. Where pipe passes

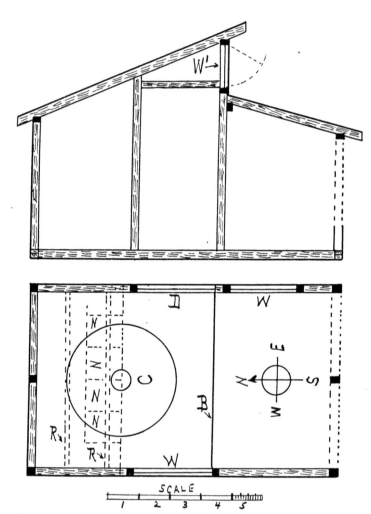

Fig. 56—Small, 6x10 ft. Woods Open Front House for back lotters. Lower or floor plan shows sills shaded, front in dotted lines, studs in back. Movable litter board (B) is used with brooder chicks. Canopy brooder (C). When brooder is removed, dropping board, roosts (R) and nests (N) as shown in dotted lines may be put in. Windows (W), door (D). Upper plan is skeleton of elevation. Monitor window (W') swings out and up. House is 4 ft. 7 in. high in rear, 7 ft. 1 in. at peak of monitor, 4 ft. 1 in. at front, over all. See text.

thru roof a flanged casting, or strong, flanged, galvanized chimney fitting, should be used to prevent leaks and to prevent hot pipe coming in contact with wood. Such castings or fittings of suitable size can be had of stove dealers, portable house dealers and those who stock poultry supplies.

Fig. 55 illustrates in outline three 10x16 houses with brooders of different types. House No. 1 carries two oil heated canopy brooders, (A). A ten inch board (B) in cleats, is used to make a smaller compartment for chicks at first. The house is divided thru the center from back to front by another 10-inch partition board (P). Blocks (X,X) are used in corners to prevent chicks crowding there. House No. 2 carries a large size canopy hover, either oil or coal heated. Corner blocks (X), partition board (B). House No. 3 carries two out-door brooders of the "Wigwarm" type with hovers (W). Middle partition about 10 inches high (P). Guide partitions, same height board, (b,b) to guide chicks to front of brooders.

Small Size Woods House

There is demand for a small open-front house of Woods type which can be used to brood chicks and later to house growing stock or a small flock of breeding fowls. Several years ago some friends of ours, who keep poultry on back lots, asked me for plans for an open-front house suitable for such use and just large enough for a flock of from 12 to 15 breeding birds. The plans were drawn, the houses built, the 6x10 ft. open-front semi-monitor house proved a success and was welcomed by back-lotters.

Fig. 56 shows this small size Woods house, indicating its use as a brooder house and as a home for adult fowls. The plan shows location of canopy brooder and a litter-board to confine chicks near hover, also, in dotted lines, are shown the roosts, dropping board and nests which may be put in place when the brooding outfit is removed. The house may be built on skids and so made portable, or it may be permanently located and set on posts or bolted to a concrete foundation. It should have a matched board floor if on skids or posts, or a concrete floor if located permanently. Building scale, showing feet and inches, is given at bottom of illustration for convenience in working out dimensions.

Lower figure is floor plan, 6 ft. wide by 10 ft. deep, sills are shown shaded except at open front where they are in dotted outline. Black squares locate the studs. Roosts (R), with dropping board (dotted line) and nests (N) under same. Door (D), windows (W), large canopy hover (C), movable 10-inch partition board in cleats (B). Upper figure is skeleton of frame and west end elevation, sills, studs and rafters shaded, except at open front where outlined in dotted lines. Monitor window (W'), hinged at top to open out and up as in other models. Black blocks locate the plates.

The side windows in this house are common 8x12 glass, six-light half sash about 24 in. square. The monitor windows are two cellar window sash, with three lights of 8x12 glass each. These windows are about 24 inches wide by 16 inches high.

Dimensions of house are 6 ft. wide by 10 ft. deep. From back wall to rear side of main stud, which supports peak of monitor, 6 ft., which gives a high rear section of proper depth, and a low front section 4 ft. deep. Height of house, over all, at rear wall is 4 ft. 7 in. Height at monitor, over all, 7 ft. 1 in.; at open front, over all, 4 ft. 1 in. Usually, at bottom of open front a 10-inch board runs the full width extending about 8 inches above top of sill. Some do not use this board but staple wire front directly to sill. For all of frame 2x3s are used with concrete foundation. On posts, 2x4 sills and floor joists. On skids, make the side sills (or skids) 2x8s and allow to extend about 18 inches back and front with lower corners a bit rounded. Use 2x4s for floor timbers. Brace open front with a bottom board 10 in. high, as above, and a top 6 in. board across width of house. Nail bottom board to side and middle studs and to sill; top board to studs and plate.

A suggestion in brooder buying; do not try to economize by buying too small a brooder, no matter what type. Get it twice as large as you expect to need. Small brooders are all right for small flocks, but it pays to have the brooding device big enough for all requirements. With a coal burning brooder stove it costs no more to keep a rather low fire in a large fire pot than it does to keep a hot fire in a small fire pot. With the larger stove you have reserve heat for emergencies when the temperature out doors takes a sudden drop to the zero mark or below. The same rule holds true with oil heated canopy brooders. Get them big enough to have ample reserve heat. It pays to do this and may save serious losses. There should be abundant reserve heating power to care for all emergencies and to insure keeping the chicks warm and comfortable.

While experienced poultrymen can handle 1000 baby chicks in one flock under one big canopy hover, few attempt it. It usually pays better to use a 1000-chick-size canopy and run it with a flock of 500 or even 300 chicks. The smaller flocks give each chick a better chance and the mortality is generally much lower.

CHAPTER IX

"The Air We Breathe"—Outdoor Natural Incubator—
Home-Made Outdoor Brooder—Brood Coops
and Other Equipment

"The beneficial effects of the action of fresh air upon our bodies and minds cannot be too strongly emphasized. Exercise and pure air dilate the air cells of the lungs, increase chest expansion, and purify the body thru stimulating the removal of waste material, thereby diminishing the possibility of illness and infection by disease germs. Mortality statistics show that the death rate of workers in indoor occupations is much higher than that of workers who are employed outdoors. The principal reason for this higher mortality rate among indoor workers is the confined air of shops and factories. The continuous inhalation of confined air is certain to exert an evil effect upon the organs of respiration and digestion, causing lassitude, fatigue, headaches, anaemia, lack of resistance, and the predisposition to catarrhal diseases. Often the sequel of such a condition is pulmonary tuberculosis and diseases of metabolism."— Floyd W. Parsons.

FOWLS HOUSED in open-front buildings, where the ventilation is good because the air is constantly and efficiently in motion, where there is abundant opportunity for the entrance of life-giving, health-promoting sunlight, where the air is not confined or artificially dried, and where the temperature is comfortable yet has the beneficial effects of moderate changes daily, following outdoor variations, are certain to be healthy and vigorous and to produce fertile and hatchable eggs, if they are well fed and otherwise given reasonably good care.

Experienced incubator operators know that to get the best results from good hatching eggs, it is necessary that the hatching room and chamber be supplied with pure, fresh air, kept in motion and carrying a reasonable amount of moisture. Air that is filled with smoke, dust, gas, vapors of kerosene and gasoline, is not pure air.

Air that is too dry or that carries excessive humidity causes discomfort. A good deal of trouble with brooder chicks is due to overheated, dry, confined air. Desert air is said to carry about 30 per cent humidity and that is uncomfortable dryness. For comfort the air should carry from 50 to 60 per cent humidity. With such a degree of moisture in the air it will require less heat to keep the body warm and comfortable than is required when the air is drier.

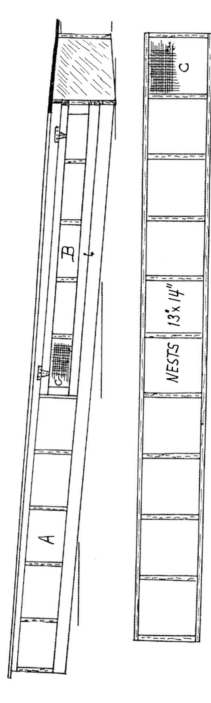

Fig. 57—Outdoor Natural-Hen Incubator. Upper plan shows front and end elevation, "A" shows nests and partitions without door, "B" shows frame of door and "C," a part of wire cloth screen used on doors. Lower plan shows ground plan of nests, each 13x14 inches, "C" shows part of wire cloth bottom. See text.

For all readers who are interested in pure air, there is a valuable article entitled "The Air We Breathe" in The World's Work, for January 1923, by Floyd W. Parsons. Following is quoted one of the closing paragraphs which should interest everybody, and particularly poultrymen:

"We hear a lot about the dangers of night air, winter air, and other kinds of air, but practically all this talk is pure bunk. Night air and winter air are no more dangerous than day air and summer air. Any natural atmosphere that is clear and undefiled is beneficial. Nothing exhibits greater ignorance than for one to shut himself in tightly and breathe the same air over and over again. The dangerous air is that which is filled with smoke, fumes, and poison gases; it is the air of winter that has been raised to a summer temperature and at the same time has not been supplied with the moisture that goes along naturally with summer air. Desert air which kills plants and animals is not as dry as that in most of our homes during the winter months. The air in many houses during the cold season altho heated to 70 degrees often contains no more than 20 per cent of saturation. Such an atmosphere is dry enough to take the life from plants and to weaken animals and humans. This artificially warmed dry air attacks the mucous membranes and makes them give up moisture so rapidly by evaporation that they are forced to neglect their natural duties and use all their powers to supply the moisture the air requires. Every breath taken makes an unnatural demand on the linings of the air passages and the result is a weakening of bodily resistance permitting the entrance of disease."

An "Outdoor" Natural Incubator

If I want to raise a large number of chickens I use incubators for hatching, also for very early chicks, but often I start eggs in a machine and finish them under hens, and frequently I give machine hatched chicks to hens to rear.

When only a hundred or so chicks are to be hatched I usually hatch and rear them under hens. Often ten or more hens are set at one time. For this purpose I use what I call an outdoor natural-hen incubator. It is usually operated outdoors in the edge of a pine grove. A ten-hen or 150 egg capacity, incubator or group of setting nests suits me best.

Fig. 57 shows building plan of the ten-hen, outdoor incubator. The lower figure is floor plan, the upper shows front and end elevation. Nest marked "C" in lower figure indicates the wire cloth (quarter-inch square-mesh galvanized netting) which forms entire bottom of the group of nests. In upper figure, "A" at left shows nest partitions, 13 inches apart, door not shown; "B" at right shows the door used to close front of nests. I make two such doors, each closing five nests. These doors are made of light two inch stuff covered with wire cloth (see "C") and hinged at top, hooked at bottom. Five hens are usually let off at one time. A screw eye is placed in the overhang of roof so that door can be hooked up while open.

To make this outdoor incubator or nest box, a back board, of inch or ⅞ inch stuff, is required 12 inches wide by 11 ft. 10 in. long; eleven partition and end pieces of same stock, 14 inches long, 15

Fig. 58—End and front view of Outdoor Natural-Hen Incubator or nest box as used in group of young white pines. Photo on author's farm.

inches high in front and 12 inches high in back. A strip of light stock for top of front 2 inches wide by 11 ft. 10 in. long. A base strip for bottom of front 3 inches wide and 11 ft. 10 in. long. Four 2 in. strips for doors, each 5 ft. 11 in. long, and four end pieces of same material 5 inches long. Four "T" hinges for front doors and four more for roof hinges. Wire cloth for bottom of nest box and for front doors.

The roof is made in one piece, of light framing stock 3 inches wide covered with heavy roofing fabric. The roof fits down over nest box giving a 3 inch overhang all around. It is hinged in front and hooked at back. For roof frame use light 3 inch stock, two pieces 12 ft. 4 in. long; two pieces 16½ in. long. Brace corners with an end strap of same material, 22½ in. long, on top of roofing at each end.

It is a good plan to bore two 1½ inch holes in top of each inside partition.

Fig. 58 shows one of these outdoor natural-hen incubators near a group of young white pines on the author's farm. The nest box has been moved out into sun for convenience in photographing, one door shown open and other closed. In use the nest box is sheltered among the pines and a portable fence of poultry wire put around the whole.

These nest boxes may be made for whatever number of nests are desired from two up to ten. For my own use I prefer the eight and ten nest sizes, particularly for use outdoors as the large boxes are not easily upset.

In winter weather they are used in an open-front house having an earth or cement floor. In spring and summer they are placed

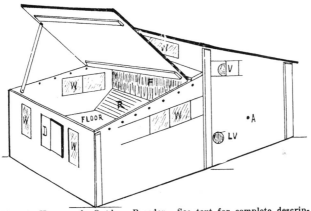

Fig. 59—Home-made Outdoor Brooder. See text for complete description. Figure shows end and side elevation.

on the ground outdoors in a sheltered spot, in the shrubbery or a group of young pines. The hatches in outdoor nests are wonderfully good. I usually put a little earth or a piece of sod in bottom at corners to round the nest, on this a thin layer of tobacco stems, and then the nest bed of soft straw or hay.

Home-Made Outdoor Brooder

The home-made outdoor brooder for which plans are given, is an old-fashioned type. When I was a youth all the boys interested in poultry used to make them, and a good many practical poultrymen too. Brooders of similar shape and type have been built and sold by many different concerns. It makes a very good brooder.

No home-made brooder has the conveniences of the well-built

tactory product, and the home-built product is seldom as well made. Usually it is better to buy brooding .equipment from a well known reliable manufacturer, but a great many people like to use tools and to build their own equipment, at least a part of it, and to satisfy the demand, these plans are given.

These brooders may be operated with the common type of brooder stove with water-pan top, or the chimneyless type of pan lamp having a "Zenith" burner. The stoves and burners can be purchased at poultry supply stores. In illustrations shown the stove used calls for a lamp chamber 9 inches high, which leaves 1½ inches in the clear between top of chimney and galvanized iron ceiling of lamp chamber. With a chimneyless "Zenith" burner lamp, there should be 3 inches in the clear between top of burner and the galvanized iron. Measure your stove or lamp and be governed accordingly, as stoves and lamps may vary in height. Some use a slide for lamp, but I prefer to set it on ground.

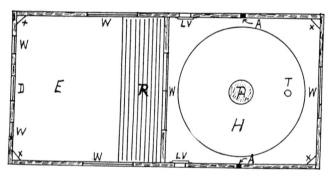

Fig. 60—Floor plan of Outdoor Brooder 3 ft. by 6 ft. 2 in. See text for full description.

Fig. 59 shows front and side elevation of the brooder, "A" is cold air intake and opens into space between galvanized iron top of lamp chamber and floor of hover chamber; "D" is door, shown open, to let chicks out of brooder; "F" is felt partition between warm rear chamber and cooler front chamber or exercising room; "R" is inclined runway; "W" windows; "LV" is 3 inch ventilating hole for lamp chamber; "V" is ventilating hole in upper part of brooder, 3 inches in diameter, covered with fine wire netting and an adjustable slide. Both front and rear lids (roofs) are hinged at middle of brooder to open upward. These lids or roofs should be covered with thin galvanized or other metal roofing, or with good roofing fabric. Windows and front and back slip into cleats inside brooder and are made snug. Usually the rear window is bedded with felt to make it tight. Monitor and side windows are each made in two pieces, to make them adjustable for additional ventilation, and slide in cleats on outside of brooder. The inside of each window is protected with fine wire netting. Door to lamp chamber is in lower part of rear wall of brooder and has a peep hole covered with mica, so that lamp can be viewed without opening door.

Fig. 60 shows floor plan of the brooder. The dimensions are 3 ft. wide by 6 ft., plus width of end boards, long. Front floor "E" is at a lower level than rear floor in hover chamber. Cold air inlets, which on outside are one inch holes, are shown in black "A"; hover "H," 30 inches in diameter; ventilating holes into lamp chamber, beneath galvanized iron, are indicated at "LV". These holes are protected on inside by bent pieces of tin covering hole at distance of about half an inch from board and open at top and bottom, (see illustration); chick door "D"; windows "W"; inclined runway "R"; shaded circle "P" indicates position of heat pipe or flue, there is no hole in the hover at this point; thermometer "T", corner cleats to stiffen brooder and prevent crowding in corners "X".

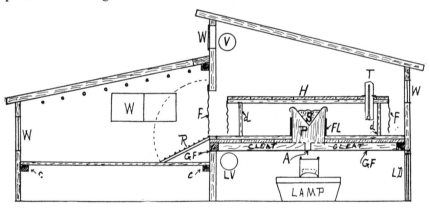

Fig. 61—End sectional view of Home-made Outdoor Brooder. Base line is 6 ft. 2 in. long and plan is drawn to scale. See text for full description.

Fig. 61 shows a side-sectional view of brooder, drawn to scale. The dimensions are 6 ft. 2 in. long, 19 inches high in front, 34 inches high at peak of monitor, 25 inches high at back. Dimensions are overall. The lamp chamber is completely enclosed on sides by the boarding and on top by a solid sheet of heavy galvanized iron, "GF", tacked to boards and cleats, and does not communicate with the brooder interior in any way. There are no holes in the galvanized ceiling or top of lamp chamber "GF"; position of lamp door "LD" in center of rear wall of chamber is indicated; ventilating hole, 3 in.

in diameter, one in each side of chamber and protected on inside by bent tin cover, previously mentioned, is shown at "LV".

The cleats between galvanized ceiling "GF" and the double floor of hover chamber are made of 1½ inch stuff. Opening "A" in side cleats communicates with one inch hole in each side of brooder for inlet of cold outdoor air. The hover chamber has a double floor made of half-inch stock, matched, laid at right angles, and should be removable, resting on but not nailed to the cleats. There is a circular hole in center of hover chamber floor to take the heat pipe or flue "P", which is nailed to it flush at bottom of floor. This gives a space above lamp, for heating fresh air, 1½ inches high and approximately 3 ft. square (less the width of cleats and side walls).

Fig. 62—Half-monitor type outdoor brooder in use during February at author's home. See text.

The heat pipe or flue "P" is made of galvanized stove pipe or tin, 6 inches in diameter, 6 inches high and open at both ends. The cone "S" is made of galvanized iron and hung to top of heat pipe "P" by three hooks which are a part of cone and spaced equally apart. The largest part of this cone "S" is 4 inches in diameter, which leaves an open space for hot air one inch wide all around the cone. The cone is kept filled with sand thoroly saturated with water. To protect the chicks the heat pipe "P" is wrapped with several thicknesses of felt or flannel "FL". The hover "H", 30 inches in diameter, is made of two layers of half-inch matched boards laid at right angles and supported by legs made of wooden dowels "d". Hover is six inches above floor and has a double fringe of felt tabs "F" all around outside reaching almost, but not quite, to floor. Brooder thermometer is shown at "T". Rear window "W" is 4x12 inches and located 6 inches above floor to give view of thermometer and light rear part of the hover chamber. Ventilating hole in peak "V" protected by screen. Monitor window "W" is 4x18 inches, screened on inside and two pieces of glass on outside to slide in cleats.

Double partition felt "F" between front and back chambers, opening here is 8 inches high by width of brooder. Floor of front chamber is 5 inches lower than hover floor. It is a single floor built on cleats and made removable. Inclined runway "R" is 10 inches by width of brooder, it is grooved or has beading strips equally spaced to make good foothold for the chicks. This runway is hinged at top and can be raised as indicated by dotted line to hook up and close rear chamber, when hooked up there should be about a half-inch space between it and partition board, to insure free circulation of air. Floor cleats "C". Side windows "W", 7 inches above floor, are protected by screen

Fig. 63—Battery of outdoor brooders with yards, in use on New Hampshire farm in early spring. Photo by author.

on inside and glass, in two pieces, slides in grooved cleats on outside, window hole dimension 5x12 inches. End windows "W", each 4x6 inches, are fastened snugly on inside by cleats. Under lid in sides of this front chamber are a number of equally spaced half-inch holes to insure free circulation of air at all times.

The heating principle is the old hot air plan, cold outdoor air is taken in at vents "A", is warmed above the galvanized iron "GF", passes up thru heat flue "P", around wet-sand-filled cone "S" from which it takes some moisture, distributed under the hover "H", passes out under and between felts "F", and thence thru partition felts "F" into front chamber which it warms to a comfortable temperature. Part of hot air is carried outside of brooder thru 3 inch ventilating hole "V" which is screened and has an adjustable slide, and part goes out thru the half-inch holes at top of sides of front chamber. Matched

white pine, cedar, or redwood is best for brooder construction.

When well built it makes a very satisfactory outdoor brooder and a comfortable well-ventilated home for small chicks. It is usual to start hover temperature at 90 to 95 degrees, with hover empty, keep the chicks comfortably warm and gradually taper off the temperature as the chicks grow. By time they are a month to five weeks old a temperature of about 75 with hover empty is usually right. But the comfort of the chicks is the only safe guide. In cold weather it is necessary to have ample reserve heat at night. Keep sand in cone "S" well saturated with water. Litter both floors with sand and cut-clover.

Fig. 64—Egg tester, common type, with box, lamp and reflector.

Brooder should be level when in operation. It should be sheltered from hot sun. Interior should be well sunned and aired daily by

Fig. 65—Home-made testing board for use in window testing by sunlight. See text.

Fig. 66—Galvanized Iron Brood Coop in use on author's farm. Note anchor stake.

opening lids and removing hover. To give chicks free access to outdoor run, a mound of earth should be built up to chick door "D" in a gentle incline. See that brooder fits earth snugly at all sides so that wind cannot blow under it.

I have operated outdoor brooders like this, and others of similar construction, outdoors in extremely cold weather and with only good results. Experience and common sense are required for successful brooder operation. Fig. 62 shows a brooder of similar type in use in February on the author's home place. Tho the temperature several times fell to zero and below the chicks grew and thrived splendidly. It was 18 degrees above zero when picture was taken by

Fig. 67—Galvanized Iron Brood Coop in use on author's farm. Note pine limbs for shade.

author. It requires skill, experience and good judgment to get satisfactory results with lamp heated outdoor brooders in zero weather.

Fig. 63 shows a group or battery of brooders of this type in use on a New Hampshire farm in the early spring, photo by author.

Egg Testers

Whether one hatches under hens or in incubators it is advisable to test the eggs on 7th and 14th days and to remove infertiles and dead germs. Sometimes when several hens are set at one time,

Fig. 68—Simple breed coop built by small boy. Photo taken on author's farm.

enough poor or infertile eggs are tested out to permit giving all the fertile eggs to a few of the hens and setting the others over again, thus saving time.

Fig. 64 shows the common box type of practical egg tester lighted by a kerosene lamp (can be lighted by electric lamp if one has electricity). Testers similar to this can be had of supply stores.

Fig. 65 shows a convenient device for daylight testing in dark room of incubator cellar or any darkened room. A window on the sunny side is partly covered with dark cloth and partly with a testing board having two felt covered holes at convenient height and distance apart. The operator can quickly pass the eggs before these holes and determine

Fig. 70—"A" type brood coop with slatted run and temporary sun and storm shelter. See text.

whether fertile, infertile, ringed, dead or containing live strong embryos. Size and development of air cell can also be noted. Sunlight makes a fine light for testing eggs. The testing board is so simple of construction that anyone can make one after examining illustration.

Fig. 69—Easily built "A" type of brood coop. See text.

Brood Coops

I usually rear chicks intended for breeders under hen mothers, whether the chicks are hen hatched or incubator chicks. For my own use I like the inexpensive, well-ventilated galvanized iron brood coops, which confine the hen and let the chicks run free.

Twine Guard Against Hawks and Crows. Chick range protected by white twine strung from wire stays, high enough for attendant to walk beneath. Said to have saved 100 times its cost by protection afforded valuable chicks. (Photo by Dr. Woods).

I think that I can buy such coops cheaper than I could build as satisfactory ones. There are so many good coops in both wood and metal offered by manufacturers, that it seems a waste of time and trouble to build such at home.

But some poultry keepers like to work with tools and have the time, and others live where they cannot conveniently go out and buy what they want and have to depend on mail order catalogs to do their shopping, so plans are offered for their benefit.

Fig. 66 shows a metal brood coop with flock of White Rock baby chicks "just out." Note that this coop is anchored by wire passed over top and made fast to stakes driven at ends, so that high winds cannot blow coop over. Fig. 67 shows another of these coops with pine limbs used to give shade. It is customary to use the pine branches more freely, but part had to be removed to get a good picture. Fig. 68 is a small box brood coop, made by a small boy, and the chicks are S. C. White Leghorns with a White Rock mother. All three photos taken on author's farm.

Fig. 69 is a very good type of apex or A-shaped brood coop. It is of such simple construction that anyone ought to be able to build one after seeing illustration. It is about 2½ ft. square at base and 2½ ft. high at peak. Sides and back are tight boarded with cleats at bottom and at peak. A board

Fig. 71—Common type Rhode Island colony brood coop. See text.

overhang is provided at front. Floor is removable and slips in on bottom cleats. Hinged to front of floor is a short drop-front which can be raised to close lower half of front at night. Upper part of front is slatted but would be better if covered with fine mesh wire cloth. With this coop is used a common A-shaped slatted coop which confines the hen and lets chicks run. To provide shade and shelter from storms a canvas or cloth tent-fly is used over the slatted coop. See Fig. 70.

All of the brood coops shown in this chapter are designed to confine the mother hen and to let the chicks run free—a very satisfactory plan. When it is necessary to confine the chicks to a wire-enclosed run, such wire run can be attached to brood coop. It is a good plan where such runs are used to have a good sized enclosure where chicks can run free and to which the hen does not have access.

An illustration herewith shows a clever plan for keeping hawks and crows away from valuable chicks. A "guard" of common twine is strung above the growing field from wire stays high enough for attendant to pass.

Fig. 71 shows a Rhode Island type of brood coop made of common boards and a six-light half-sash window. The dimensions of this coop are 2½ ft. square floor measure, 2½ ft. high. Floor is removable.

BROODER PLANS IN CHAPTER IX

In 1904, E. Pryce Mitchell, Santa Barbara, California, Master-Mariner and successful poultryman, author of "A Practical Poultry Plant for Southern California," wrote: "To Dr. Woods' brooder belongs a large part of my success."

CHAPTER X

More Discussion of Fresh Air—Moisture in the Air—Fowls Prefer Open-Front House—Comfort Brood Coop—Harris Open-Air Roost—Young's Colony Coop—Tolman's Open-Air Coop

"Some people think that we do not need to trouble ourselves about ventilating a room when it is large. They believe that there is air enough in it to last a long time. But this is a mistake. To be sure, the air lasts a little longer in a large room than in a small one; still after an hour or so the people in it need to have just as much pure air come in and impure air go out as if they were in a small room. Whenever you go into a house from out of doors **take special pains to notice how the air smells. Notice it when you first go in,** because each one of us gets used to air after we have been in it awhile, and then we cannot tell whether it is pure or impure. If it really has any odor, or if it does not seem pleasant as compared to the air out of doors, you may know that it is not pure.
"If everything is shut you are breathing impure air and you ought to do something about it."—L. H. Gulick, M. D.

NEARLY one thousand years ago, according to a lecture before the French Academy of Medicine by Dr. Dinguizli of Tunis, the ancient Arab physician Avicenna recognized, described and successfully treated tuberculosis. The main essentials of his treatment were fresh air, substantial feeding including plenty of milk, rest of body and mind, and prolonged sleep. He also particularly recommended that crabs and other crustaceans be used largely in the diet, and he used the shells as medicine because of their mineral content, which is largely carbonate and phosphate of lime.

Truth lives long, altho often it takes a long time for the truth to be appreciated or accepted. This ancient Arab physician was more modern in some of his methods than many people of today. We still have with us those who are afraid of fresh air, who clamor loudly about the danger of overfeeding, who do not appreciate the value of milk and its indispensable vitamins, and who have not yet learned the need for and value of mineral foods.

Answer to a Critic

In Chapters VI and VIII I quoted from the experience of a number of poultrymen who have been very successful with open-front poultry houses in severely cold climates. A man in New York state, I withhold his name, after reading about open-front houses, quite vigorously disagrees with me on several points. Evidently he reads hastily and carelessly and jumps at conclusions. Following are quotations from part of his letter:

"Well, such open-front houses as Prince T. Woods describes are all right in their proper climates, but for him to state that such houses are advisable in climates where it is 40 below zero, makes one wonder if he does not need to see a physician, for houses in such cold climates as that would not only mean frozen combs, but quite likely frozen feet and quite likely birds frozen to death on their perch and to say the least it would be a good case for the Humane Society.

"I personally should prefer to clean the dropping board daily. Human beings like to pass over all extra jobs that they can, and the practice of cleaning out hen houses is small enough anyway without Prince T. Woods advising that it be neglected. It is human nature to be lazy, many are glad of his advice of neglect.

"I have healthy birds the year 'round and I have no trouble in getting winter eggs, but my houses are cleaned daily. An entirely open-front house where it is 40 below zero is only for a lazy man and a hard hearted creature as well.

"For him to tell us that 'A strong wind blowing against the front of an open-front poultry house is met and overcome by a perfect air cushion on the inside, which turns back the wind, no matter how strong it may blow' sounds quite flowery but what poultrymen need is sound logic. The above all depends on the direction of the wind.

"I have friends in the western part of Canada where it is 40 degrees below zero, where the air is so dry that you do not notice it is so cold, but it would only take a short time for your ears to become frozen, and to constantly be on the watch is indeed not putting it too strong and when I compare that climate with March on the coast of Massachusetts, and read that Dr. Woods' plan is for all climates, well many a poultryman of the north will wink one eye as he reads it but will pass it by for something more sound, something that rings true."—E. S.

I have not quoted all of Mr. "E. S.'s" letter, there is a good deal more of it along the same line. He seems to have taken a violent dislike to me personally as well as to the subject. He was really so much disturbed that he could not read straight or carefully, for which I am sorry, for I really am not "a lazy man and a hard hearted creature." Quite the opposite.

A part of what excites Mr. S. was quoted by me from an article by James B. Morman, a poultry expert of wide experience—that part relative to 40 degrees below zero and about the air cushion. Both of these matters have been further explained in Chapter VIII, and confirmed by abundant testimony, including the Department of Agriculture of British Columbia report for 1909, a physician in Toronto, Canada, and experienced poultrymen in Alberta and in Quebec. The "air cushion" is also further explained in that chapter. I hope that Mr. S. has not been too prejudiced to read it carefully, he might learn something helpful, even tho it may at first conflict with his opinions. Anyone who cares to do so can demonstrate for himself the fact of the "air cushion" without the need of building a house. Go into any room that can be tightly closed and that has a window on the windy side. See that the room is tightly closed on all sides, then open the window wide. Standing near to the open window the pressure of the wind outside can be distinctly felt blowing in. Then slip a well-fitted mosquito screen into the open window and immediately the pressure of the outside wind seems less and it cannot be felt at all a short distance from the window. Of course the success of the experiment depends upon the walls and doors being tight and snug except for the front where window is open. In a properly built open-front house the air cushion as described and illustrated in Chapter VIII can be demonstrated easily and satisfactorily.

So far as the "Humane Society" is concerned, agents of the Society for the Prevention of Cruelty to Animals investigated open-front poultry houses thoroly a long time ago, in 1904 or 1905 if I remember rightly, and pronounced them satisfactory and desirable. Since then such open-front houses have been endorsed by representatives of several governments. One of the best things about an open-front poultry house is that it is more comfortable and more humane than the average type closed house, also it is practically "fool proof."

I think that every poultry keeper safely can be left to decide for himself how often he will clean poultry houses and dropping boards. It is his business not mine. Of course where dropping boards are used they should be cleaned sufficiently often to prevent accumulations of droppings becoming offensive. It is difficult to keep the wood of dropping boards in sanitary condition no matter how often they may be cleaned.

Most of my houses are not provided with dropping boards, and such really seem more sanitary to me. In these houses the droppings fall to the floor beneath the roosts where they are quickly covered with sand, earth and litter which the fowls scratch over them. Fowls usually scratch with their heads toward the light and so throw a good deal of absorbent material toward the rear of the house. Under such conditions very frequent cleaning is not necessary.

Where one has large flocks, or is busy with more important matters, every means of saving labor counts and it is wise to avoid spending too much time on unnecessary work. If the fowls are healthy and well fed, most of the droppings will be rather dry and formed, and such do not so quickly heat or become offensive.

I know a good many successful, practical poultrymen who do not use dropping boards in their poultry houses. One of these men has about 2000 layers and does all of his own work. He cleans out his poultry houses regularly spring and fall and oftener if the droppings become offensive. He says that he can depend upon his nose to tell him when the houses need cleaning and that he has no use for dropping boards and no time to waste fussing with them. I think he knows what he is talking about for I have visited his plant often and his houses are always in good sanitary condition and free from offensive odors. His fowls are healthy and productive.

Recently I was in a plaster-finished closed-type poultry house where the dropping boards are scraped clean daily and sprinkled with earth. The house was decidedly smelly tho apparently clean. The manure-saturated wood of the dropping board, which has been treated frequently with disinfectants, contributed largely to the stench. I would not want a house like that and would find it unpleasant to work in one, but it seemed to suit the owner, and as he appeared so well satisfied I made no comment.

Mr. S.'s terrible picture of birds frozen to death on their perches and other birds with frozen combs and frozen feet, does credit to his, or is it her, imagination, but it will bring smiles to the faces of users of open-front poultry houses and serve to amuse readers who have carefully read the preceding chapters, particularly the testimony concerning the Single Comb White Leghorns of William McKenzie in Alberta, Canada. All closed houses there sent out frozen combs every winter but there were no frozen combs in the open-front houses. Comb freezing is largely a matter of condition of the fowl. If it is in poor health or lacks resistance from other cause it may become an easy victim.

So far as birds freezing to death is concerned that is all rank nonsense. Well-fed, well-kept birds will not freeze to death in open-front houses or even when roosting in evergreen trees. If they are sick or half starved that is a different matter. Our wild birds do not freeze to death unless they are sick or unable to get food enough to keep them in good order, and the same is true of domestic fowls.

I hope that Mr. S. may overcome his indignation and prejudice sufficiently to study the subject of fresh-air housing and carefully read this and the preceding chapters. It is a great pity for him to waste his evidently abundant energy pawing the air and calling names. If he could be convinced and become a fresh-air booster, he would be a winner.

In the same mail with Mr. S.'s letter came the following:

"Dear Sir:—I read with much interest Dr. Woods' open-front house article. I have a flock of Rocks and Reds, 32 in all, in an open-front house here where the temperature falls as low as 30 degrees below zero, and am getting from 17 to 20 eggs a day.

(Signed)   Albert B. Gross."

There you are, friend Reader, if you want to get facts about open-front houses "ask the man who uses them." Mr. Gross' letter, which reached me at the same time, is a pretty good answer to Mr. S.'s attack.

Moisture in the Air

In Chapter IX, I said that "For comfort the air should carry from 50 to 60 per cent humidity." To avoid misunderstanding on the part of the reader, perhaps that statement should be more clearly explained.

The amount of moisture in the atmosphere is determined by an instrument called a hygrometer and is expressed in percentages as relative humidity. If the relative humidity is 50 per cent, the air contains half the moisture which would be required to saturate it. The higher the temperature the more moisture required to saturate the air. Hot moist air seems much warmer than dry air of same temperature; cold moist air seems colder than dry air of the same temperature.

A relative humidity of from 50 to 60 per cent would be **dry air,** a lower percentage of saturation than 50 per cent is very dry and soon becomes uncomfortable. A relative humidity of 65 to 75 per cent is called **moderate,** from that up to 85 per cent is **moderately damp,** while above 85 per cent is **very damp.**

It is not uncommon where brooders are operated by inexperienced persons, particularly where the chicks are confined indoors, to have complaints of chicks with legs and feet "dried up and withered" and bodies ill nourished. Often the trouble is attributed to the warm floors, to food, and to other causes. While the trouble in part may be due to lack of good care and to faulty feeding, a larger part of the cause will be found to be **too dry air** in the brooder and exercising room. Frequently the atmosphere of the brooding quarters only carries from 20 to 30 per cent humdity, which is the killing dryness of a desert and fatal to living things. Kept in such dangerously dry atmosphere the chicks literally dry up, have the normal moisture dried out of them, and, of course, are also ill nourished no matter how liberally fed. The remedy is to provide for more moisture in the air, evaporate moisture from water pans attached to the heater or from trays of wet sand, and to get the chicks onto an outdoor run as soon as they can be trained to use it.

One of the best individual brooders, of the outdoor type, that I have ever seen provides for both hot-air and hot-water heating and a vent from the hot-water tank discharges enough moisture into the brooding quarters to supply a sufficiently high relative humidity for health and comfort.

Thru mistaken "kindness" too many people coddle their chicks and make them tender and delicate, easy victims to all ailments. It is far more kind to gradually harden the chicks as they grow, to accustom them to running outdoors in all sorts of weather, and to so train them that they can not only take good care of themselves in both storm and sunshine but also learn to be "hawk-shy" and quickly run to cover when danger threatens.

The pampered, petted and much coddled chick is always a liability and ever in danger, while the well-trained, properly-hardened chick is an asset, able to take care of itself under all ordinary conditions, has ample resistance and is seldom in danger.

Fowls Prefer Open-Front House

Some interesting observations concerning the housing of poultry by Prof. James Dryden, are contained in Oregon Agricultural College bulletin No. 80, for June 1913, from which I quote the following:

"Housing has considerable to do with the health and vigor of the stock. Ages ago, before domestication, chickens roosted in trees, and they still have a little of the wild nature. Did you ever notice when the curfew of the poultry-yard summons the chickens to their roosts that they usually go to bed on the branches of a tree if there is one nearby? Not long ago I watched a large flock of fine chickens near Corvallis retire for the night. The farmer had built good houses for the flock, but near the houses there was a giant oak tree decorated by nature with mistletoe; one after another the hens flew into this tree, some hopping from one branch to another until they reached the top-most branches, higher than the highest barn on the farm. It was interesting to see the chickens nestle down under the mistletoe for the night while the roosts in the poultry houses were vacant.

"It is the nature of the hen to roost in the tree rather than in the house, and the poultryman should study her nature if he wishes to succeed.

"On another occasion I watched a flock of hens retire for the night where they had the choice of two houses. One was a sort of shed affair with one side about all open; it was a fresh-air house. The other was a closed house with a few small holes for ventilation. About nine out of every ten of the hens crowded into the open house, tho they had originally been equally divided between the two houses. They preferred the fresh-air house. If there had been a tree in the yard they probably would have preferred that to either of the houses.

"There are times, of course, in severe storms when chickens prefer the shelter of a roof to roosting in a tree; but the lesson is, that fowls prefer the outdoor-life, or the 'simple life,' and when we put them in close houses and compel them to live there under the mistaken notion that we are being good to them, we are imposing conditions that will result in decreased vitality. Housing is really an artificial condition for chickens and it is a serious mistake in poultry keeping to follow too closely artificial lines.

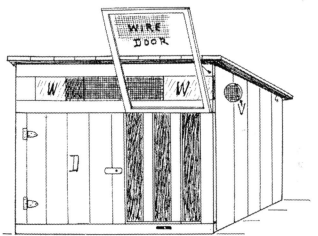

Fig. 72—"Comfort" Brood Coop for hen and chicks, 3 ft. long by 2½ ft. deep, 2½ ft. high in front and 20 inches high at rear. Door "D"; adjustable glass slides "W" over ventilating window; 3 inch ventilating hole "V." See text.

"It should not be concluded, however, from what has been said above, that the best kind of housing for chickens is in the trees. It should not be inferred, either, that we should avoid all so-called artificial methods in poultry keeping. While housing may be an artificial condition for fowls, nevertheless good housing is necessary if we wish to get the greatest profit."

Prof. Dryden's observations, quoted above, are interesting and sound. Many times I have noticed flocks of young and old stock giving preference to open-front quarters when closed houses were

Fig. 73—Rhode Island chick growing field with colony brood coops. See text.

close by in which a part of the flock had been confined for some time.

While I have had fowls from closed houses take to roosting in the trees, it is very unusual for fowls quartered in fresh-air houses. There are trees close by several of my open-front houses, and the birds often roost on the branches during the hot part of the day or when resting, but at bed time all of the flock retire to the roosts in the open-front house.

Often in summer I have wired in a part of a pine grove and kept fowls there without other shelter than the evergreen trees all summer long. Roofed nest boxes were provided, but the hens always roosted on the limbs of the pines. I found it a splendid way to keep breeding stock in fine order all thru the hot weather. The practice was discontinued only because chicken thieves have become so troublesome during the past few seasons with the increased use of automobiles. Foxes, big owls and a pair of eagles also gave us quite a little trouble the last season we let the fowls "camp out," so now all flocks are housed thruout the year in open-front houses and locked up at night.

Another interesting statement by Prof. Dryden, in the bulletin named above, is this:

"Fowls require considerably more fresh air than farm animals. It has been estimated that a hen in proportion to her weight requires double the weight of oxygen that a man or horse requires. The amount of air breathed per 1000 pounds live weight of hens is given by King as 8,272 cubic feet in 24 hours; the requirements of a man being 2,833 and a cow 2,804 cubic feet. Ventilation, moreover, keeps the house dry. A close, warmly built house, with glass windows, is always damp, because of the extremes of temperature between day and night. Dampness is overcome by ventilation. Ventilation can be best furnished by leaving one end or one side open or partly open."

"Comfort" Brood Coop

The "Comfort" Brood Coop shown in Fig. 72 is designed for comfort for the chicks and convenience for the care-taker. It is rather larger than most brood coops intended for one hen and her brood, and will accommodate a hen and 25 chicks very comfortably. The hen is confined to the coop, the chicks run free or have a wire enclosure attached to the coop.

This coop is 3 ft. long by 2½ ft. deep. It is 2½ ft. high in front and 20 inches high in rear. The roof is made on cleats, boarded up and down, hinged at front to open upward, and is covered with any good roofing fabric. It fastens down with hooks at back. This roof has an overhang of about 3 inches all around. End walls and back are made of matched box boards, nailed to light cleats, and put on up and down as shown. For bottom cleats 2x2s are used. The floor is of same matched boards built on cleats and made to fit inside of coop so as to be easily removable. In each end near roof at front is a 3 inch ventilating hole marked "V", covered on inside with fine mesh galvanized wire netting. The front of coop is boarded on horizontal at top and bottom as shown, balance up and down. At left is shown a door "D", hinged at left to open out; this door is about 15½ inches wide by 19½ inches high. A slatted opening is shown at right; this is covered at night by a wire screen door 14 inches wide by 19½ inches high. Use quarter-inch square-mesh galvanized wire cloth in making this door. Screen door hooks up out of way when coop is open and is buttoned down with a strap-iron button when door is closed.

At top of front two pieces of window glass "W", each 4½x9 inches, side in grooves made by the match of the boarding, and cover a ventilating window which is 4 inches high by 18 inches long. On inside of coop this window is covered with fine mesh galvanized wire netting. This gives an adjustable ventilating window in addition to wire door; the glass slides permit any adjustment desired.

Painted with a good oil paint on outside and a good disinfectant on inside, this coop will last many years and can be kept free from mites with ordinary care.

Fig. 73 shows a chick growing field in Rhode Island equipped with a type of brood coop which is common in that section. These coops are 3 ft. long, 2½ ft. wide, 20 inches high at eaves and 2½ ft. high at peak. They have removable floors built on cleats. These coops are made of common boards and cracks are battened with lath. A sliding window and sliding wire screen are used to close the front opening. The coop is so simple of construction that anyone should be able to build it after looking at the illustration.

Brood coops of this type and others of similar pattern are commonly used on Rhode Island farms. The mother hens are usually confined to the coops and the chicks enjoy liberal range. As the hen mothers start an alarm on the approach of hawks and other varmints, the chicks quickly get "hawk-shy" and "danger-shy" and the losses are very few. The mortality from all causes is very low. It is no uncommon sight to see 2000 to 3000 young chicks, in flocks of 25 to a hen, housed in such brood coops and having practically free range. Those who are alarmed by the alleged dangers of free range would be surprised to see these remarkable free range flocks and to learn that from all causes the losses in any flock are very small and in some broods there is no loss at all.

The Harris Open-Air Roost

The Harris Open-Air Roost for weaned chicks, was designed by W. S. Harris, successful poultryman, of Mansfield, Mass. It has been used with excellent results for small chicks as early as they are able to do without artificial heat or have been weaned by the hen mother. Mr. Harris used it with good results for June hatched chicks which had been carried for the first three weeks in a cold brooder. In cool weather the chicks to use this roost should be from five to seven weeks old. In mild warm weather it provides weaning quarters for month old chicks. When small chicks are first put in this roost, Mr. Harris uses cylinders of half-inch mesh poultry wire to separate the chicks into small groups to prevent crowding, not more than 25 in each.

Fig. 74 gives building plans for a 4x4 Harris Open-Air Roost to accommodate 100 weaned chicks or 50 half-grown chickens. The frame

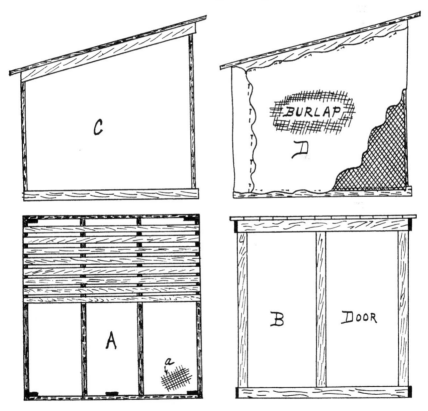

Fig. 74—The Harris Open-Air Roost for weaned chicks. Dimensions 4x4 ft. floor plan "A"; 4x4 front elevation "B"; side elevation of frame, 4 ft. high in front and 3 ft. high at back "C." In floor plan "A" a part of frame is shown with roosts of lath or planed furring which cover whole floor spaced about an inch apart. Wire screen bottom on under side of frame is indicated at "a". In elevation "D" method of pinning burlap sacking with wire nails to netting side walls is shown. A part of burlap is cut away to show the galvanized wire netting sides. See text.

is made of 1x3 inch furring, preferably spruce, and the roof is of matched box boards. The ground plan is "A" and is about 4x4 ft. As indicated the floor frame is built with one-inch side of furring up. Black oblongs indicate the uprights or studs. The entire bottom of frame is covered with inch-mesh wire netting "a" (galvanized). Lath or planed furring is used for the roosts which are put on about one inch apart to cover whole floor—in illustration they are shown on about half of floor frame.

The front frame is shown marked "B", side frame "C". This roost is built 4 ft. high in front and 3 ft. high at back, plus the roof boards. Half of the front has a door of 1x3 stuff covered with one-inch mesh wire netting. Entire coop is enclosed in one-inch mesh galvanized wire netting.

At night and on cold windy days common burlap sacking is placed about the coop, covering in part or all of the wire netting. Usually the door is left uncovered except on very cool nights. This burlap cover is indicated on plan marked "D", a part of burlap is cut away in illustration to show the wire netting beneath. This burlap is not tacked on, but is pinned to the netting with wire nails, so that it can be quickly put on or taken off, see Fig. 74, "D".

As a rule the burlap cover is used until the chicks are well feathered. When they have made good growth and the weather is mild, the front wire is seldom covered with burlap unless weather is stormy.

For small chicks the roost should sit on the ground. For well-feathered, half-grown chicks, the roost should be put on supports about six to eight inches above the ground to give better circulation of air. In a windy location the roost should be anchored by driving

Fig. 75—Part of a row of Dan Young's Fresh-Air Colony Coops as used for many years on his farm at Monroe, N. Y. See text.

two stakes, one at each end, and passing baled hay wire over top of roost coop and fastening same to both stakes. A sheltered place in an orchard makes a good location.

This roost coop is easily cleaned. Most of the droppings fall thru between roosts to wire netting bottom. Clean with a stiff broom and then move the coop to fresh ground. Sun the whole coop often. If necessary it can be washed with a hose and then dried in the sun.

Where one does not find it convenient to transfer weaned chicks directly from brood coop or brooder to an open-front poultry house, this Harris Open-Air Roost makes very satisfactory and inexpensive growing quarters for summer flocks.

Use only good strong galvanized wire netting, either half-inch or inch mesh, and be sure to use it on bottom of coop frame below the roosts. This is necessary in order to make the roost coop rat proof.

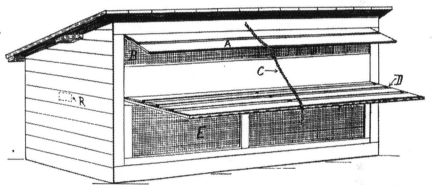

Fig. 76—Detail elevation plan of D. W. Young's fresh-air colony coop for growing stock. Dimensions are 3x6 ft. floor measure, 3½ ft. high in front and 2½ ft. high at back. Upper front shutter "A" built like a window blind; upper ventilating window, screened, 8 inches high by 5½ ft. long. "B"; chain for adjusting shutters "C"; lower shutter built of clapboards like a window blind, "D"; hinged screen door, 18 inches high by 5½ ft. long, "E"; dotted lines indicating position of roost "R". See text.

Dan Young's Fresh-Air Colony Coop

For many years everybody knew about Dan Young's White Leghorns and their winnings at Madison Square Garden, but comparatively few people knew that Mr. Young used fresh-air colony coops for his growing stock.

Fig. 75 shows a view of end of a long row of these colony coops on D. W. Young's farm, Monroe, N. Y., photo by author. In a big field, where the young stock had free range, there were, at time photo was taken in 1915, one hundred of these fresh-air colony coops in one long row at top of a sunny slope.

Fig. 76 is detail elevation plan of the Young Fresh-Air Colony

Fig. 77—Tolman's Open-Air Growing Coops in field on plant of Joseph Tolman, Rockland, Mass. Photo by author. See text.

Coop. This coop is 3x6 ft. floor measure, 3½ ft. high in front and 2½ ft. high in back. The roof hinges at front to lift up and hooks at back. Roof has a generous overhang all around. The coop is built mainly of novelty siding, except where noted. Floor is matched boards on cleats and is removable. Upper front shutter "A" is made of cedar clapboards on cleats and is hinged at top to swing out and up. There is a three-quarter inch space for air between the upper and lower clapboards, like a window blind, so that when shutter is down snug there is ventilation at this point. The space "B" is 8 inches high by 5 feet 6 inches long and is covered on inside of coop with galvanized netting quarter-inch square mesh. Shutter "A" is seldom closed.

The chain "C" hooks over a wire screw hook on shutters "A" and "D" and screen door "E", making them adjustable at any height desired. Shutter "D" is built of four cedar clapboards on cleats, with a three-quarter inch space between the clapboards like a window blind as indicated to admit air and keep out rain or snow. This shutter is hinged at top to swing out and up as shown.

Screen door "E", 18 inches by 5 feet 6 inches, is made of quarter-inch mesh galvanized netting on a frame of 1x2 in. furring. This screen door is hinged at top to swing out and up under shutter "D", and has a hook to engage chain "C". When this screen door "E" and shutter "D" are swung wide open and fastened in position, it permits the whole flock to run out and in without any danger of crowding or damage to plumage.

When chickens are old enough to need a roost, a single 2x3 roost is used on cleats in about center of house, bottom of roost 18 inches above bottom of coop. Position of roost is shown in Fig. 76 at dotted lines marked "R". Anyone who can make a box should be able to build this coop.

Joe Tolman's Open-Air Coop

I told about the Tolman Fresh-Air house in use on Joe Tolman's fresh air poultry plant, Rockland, Mass., in Chapter V. The Tolman open-air growing coop for half grown chicks is a part of his regular equipment. Fig. 77 is reproduced from the author's photograph of part of a row of these coops on the growing range on Joseph Tolman's farm.

Fig. 78 shows detail elevation plan of front and one side of this open-air coop and also floor plan 10x10 ft. with studding indicated in black squares. Framing material for this coop is 2x3 in. stuff. In elevation plan the black oblongs locate the position of the 2x3 rafters which are horizontal. Roof is of matched boards put on up and down. There are no sills under studding. The studs or uprights in frame are fastened together at base by a 9 or 10 inch board all around as indicated.

This coop is 10x10 ft. floor measure, 5 ft. 8 in. high at peak, 3 ft. 4 in. high at corners. The roof has a generous overhang of about 18 inches front and back

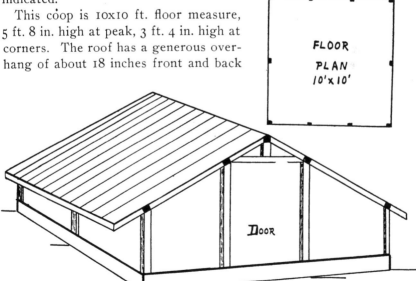

Fig. 78—Side and front elevation detail of Tolman's Open-Air Growing Coop, also floor plan. Black oblongs in elevation indicate location of rafters. Black squares in floor plan indicate studs or uprights. Dimensions 10x10 ft. floor, 5 ft. 8 in. high at peak, 3 ft. 4 in. high at corners. See text.

and at eaves. There is a door 3 ft. wide by 4 ft. high at both front and back.

Doors are of one-inch mesh hexagon galvanized poultry netting on spruce frames of 1x2 in. stuff. All sides are made of same one-inch mesh hexagon galvanized wire netting.

The floor is built separately. It is of matched boards on three pieces of 2x4 inch frame stuff placed 2 inch side up. This floor is built and cut to fit the coop so that upper portion of coop can be let down over floor. Ordinary cleaning can be done with a long handled hoe from both doors. For thoro cleaning the coop can be jacked up from floor and pushed over on one end out of the way, giving free access to all parts.

The construction is so simple that anyone should be able to build after viewing illustrations. Can be made six or eight feet square if desired. No roosts are used until chickens are well grown. When roosts are desired, place one on each side of door, made of 2x3 stuff, in cleats about 2 ft. above floor. By putting cleats across from end studding on either side of door, two roosts can be placed on each side if desired. This open-air growing coop has given excellent results for many seasons.

CHAPTER XI

Large Flock Units—Semi-monitor Open-Front Houses for 200 Fowls—House for 500 Fowls—Good Breaking-Up Coop for Broodies

"Man and beast may live three weeks without food, three days without water, and three minutes without air. The principle of fresh air poultry housing is sound. But build the house deep, not shallow."—A. P. J., April, 1923.

THE ADVICE quoted above is good. Deep houses are much to be preferred to shallow ones; as a rule, are more comfortable, convenient and economical. But fowls have frequently been wintered successfully—kept in good health and delivered good egg yield—in comparatively shallow open-front houses in a severe climate.

It is surprising how well fowls will winter in severe northern climates with no other house than an open-front shed in poor repair and with cracks on all sides for the wind to blow thru. In such a house with a closed front they would be victims of disease. In the fall of 1922 I had about two dozen surplus cockerels, Black Langshans, that I intended to use for table purposes thru the winter. The most convenient place to confine them was in an old 20x20 open-front house, much out of repair. This building had been used several seasons as a hog house and the hogs had damaged it considerably. It was built of matched boards and those on sides showed many cracks. The side windows had been taken out. The roofing had been carried away in part from the front roof, tho rear roof was tight. While the house was in use for hogs a partition fence, from front to back made of 2x3s thru middle of house, had been put in. I made no repairs and no changes. Just put the cockerels into the house and kept them there, keeping them always supplied with food and water.

These were big husky birds, 9 to 10 pounds each, with good sized combs and wattles. They roosted by preference on the partition fence up near the front, and, as the windows were out of sides, they had breezy sleeping quarters. Altho we had a very severe winter and much zero and below zero weather, down to 27 degrees below zero once and ten to fifteen degrees below a number of times, not one of these birds ever had a cold or even frosted comb or wattles. We used one for roasting every little while. They kept in very good order with practically no care at all. The last of March we still had five of them left, having eaten or sold the rest. These, with what hens are culled out for table use, will serve to supply roast fowl for the family table until there are plenty of young chickens.

I believe in having good houses and prefer open-front houses that are deep from front to back, but the experience related above shows that birds will winter alright in very wide-open buildings and that the timid, who fear for the comfort of their flocks, need not worry about fowls in a well-built modern open-front building.

Semi-monitor open-front houses of the Woods type are described and illustrated in detail in Chapters III, VI and VIII, giving plans, dimensions and building instructions for the popular sizes.

In American Poultry Journal for April, 1923, Frank L. Platt discusses "Poultry Science at Iowa Agricultural College" and describes a 22x24 ft. semi-monitor open-front farm poultry house for flock of 150, which has proven satisfactory at the Iowa College. This house is 24 feet wide and 22 feet deep, 5 ft. high front and rear, 9 ft. 6 in. high at peak of monitor. The front of main studding supporting monitor and front of rear roof, is 14 ft. from rear wall along line of sill; from main stud to open-front 8 ft. Open front is boarded up at bottom higher than is customary with my houses, the open space in front is figured at one square foot of opening for each ten square feet of floor space. In proportions and essentials this house is of the Woods type as plans were first published in 1908 and 1909. Where I hinge monitor windows at top to open out, the house at Iowa College has monitor windows hinged at bottom to open in and recommends that these windows be opened about 1 to 2 ft. in summer and about 4 inches in winter, except during blizzard weather when they are closed.

Prof. H. A. Bittenbender, in charge of poultry husbandry at Iowa College, is quoted as saying:

"The semi-monitor poultry house appears to be a good practical house for the general farm because it contains those principles of construction which are essential for successful poultry production. First of all it has the floor space arranged so that it will be most practical and beneficial for the poultry flock during the winter months. The principle of ventilation is maintained in the best possible manner. Sunlight can readily gain access in almost all parts of this house. Its cost when compared with other types of houses is not much greater and for the few additional dollars that it may cost in construction it will pay good interest in the form of healthy poultry."

A novel and excellent floor has been introduced in this Iowa-built semi-monitor house. First a six inch fill-in is made with gravel and leveled off. On top of this is laid a floor of hollow-tile blocks, each 4 in. x 8 in. x 12 in., which resist moisture. An inch of smooth concrete, rich in cement, is laid on top of the tile to finish the floor. The foundation walls, to which sills are bolted, are of concrete. (See Chapter II). Before laying sills in concrete it is wise to give them a good coat of wood-preserving creosote or as-phaltum and let it dry in.

Large Flock Units

The large flock units of from 200 to 500 and even 1000 or more layers, kept together under one roof, are popular with some prac-tical poultrymen who keep fowls chiefly for production of market eggs. Tho some of these large flocks have liberal outdoor range, many of them are not supplied with yards and are kept confined to the houses, being marketed as soon as thru the season's laying and replaced with other layers. As a rule no males are kept with the flocks as infertile eggs are desired.

The big flock unit on a large plant does save a good deal of labor. It is supposed to be economical of housing space and to have other advantages. Personally, I think there are serious disadvant-ages in very large flocks. In big units the fowls do not get to know one another as well as in smaller ones and the attendant does not have the same opportunity to observe individuals. The health risk is greater. If disease starts it is difficult to control. I do not like to have "all the eggs in one basket."

I have carried both big and little flocks. I think that there is a limit to the size of the flock unit beyond which the decrease in production and the risk of loss makes it unwise to go, except under exceptionally favorable climate and conditions. Observing the work of others and from my own experience, I prefer flock units not to exceed 150 layers for heavy breeds and 200 layers for light weight breeds.

For breeding purposes I get very satisfactory results from flocks of 40 to 100 fowls. Such flocks are comfortably taken care of in the popular sizes of open-front houses.

However, there are a number of people who want bigger hous-es and desire to use the semi-monitor type open-front house. In this chapter tested plans are given for such houses to provide for large flocks of from 150 to 200 and 400 to 500 layers respectively.

I have not used either of these large houses but they have been tried out on farms where I have had opportunity to note results.

House for 200 Hens

The 24x24 ft. semi-monitor open-front house is designed to accommodate 150 fowls of the large breeds or 200 fowls of the smaller or Mediterranean breeds.

In some of the house plans in preceding chapters the illustrations show only a sufficient number of roosts to accommodate capacity of house for a small breed. Obviously if the house is to be used for medium or large breeds it will be necessary to add more roost space. Usually it is safe to figure in length of roost 6 inches to each bird for Mediterraneans, 7 to 8 inches per bird for American breeds and 8 to 9 inches for Asiatics. However, with big Langshans I find that 15 fowls, including a husky 11 pound male, can comfortably perch on a roost 10 feet long, that is 8 inches per large fowl and they seem to have ample room for comfort.

In any of the house plans shown in this or the preceding chapters the furnishings are not arbitrary. Several styles of furnishing poultry houses are shown. Every poultry keeper has views of his own on this subject, and a number of men I know seem to take a lot of satisfaction in changing over the interior arrangement of their poultry houses.

The number of nests and their location is another matter that often comes up for discussion. An allowance of one 13x14 inch nest for every 5 or 6 hens is usually ample where the flock is large. For small flocks of 6 to 10 hens I would not provide less than 3 nests. Where a large number of nests are provided it will be noted that some nests are more preferred than others and 8 or 10 hens may use the same nest while other nests are seldom occupied.

The location of nests and other furnishings should be made to avoid shutting off floor space or interfering with light and ventilation. Some object to nests under the dropping board. It does call for constant vigilance to prevent mites harboring there. For my own houses I prefer to do without the dropping board, as a rule. I like to arrange nests in banks or tiers on side walls, well up from floor to allow head-room for fowls underneath. I find that my Asiatics will take in the fourth tier in such a bank of nests without the need of a poultry ladder.

Fig. 79 shows the side elevation frame plan and detail for the 24x24 ft. semi-monitor open-front house.

Scale is given to aid in working out special dimensions. The sill is a 4x4 timber 24 ft. long. The front and back studs are 2x4s each 5 ft. long. The "main stud," which supports monitor and front of rear roof, is a 4x4 and the center of this stud is 14 ft. from rear wall. There are four of these "main studs" each 10 ft. 3 inches long. The black square "T" beneath the rafters indicates a 4x4 girder which runs under rafters full width of house to give added support to rear roof. The stud which holds up this girder is also a 4x4. There are four of these studs each 7 ft. 9 in. long. See "A,A" in Fig. 80 for location of four main studs and four studs supporting girder.

The overall dimensions of this house in height are 5 ft. 11 in. front and rear on line of studs; 11 ft. 3 in. at peak of monitor; 7ft. 9 in. at rear of front roof.

In Fig. 79 the 2x4 plate to support rafters of rear part of front roof is shown at "P", spiked to front side of main studs. The outline marked "B" indicates a brace plate of 2x4 between the main

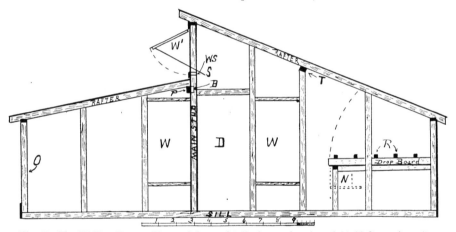

Fig. 79—The 200-Hen House. Plan and frame detail of east elevation of 24x24 ft. semi-monitor poultry house. See text.

studs and spiked to them and to the plate "P". Outline at "WS" is the sill at bottom of monitor windows. Monitor window "W'", shown open, is a half sash of six 8x12 in. lights. Each window is about 2 ft. 3 in. x 2 ft. 4 in. There are six of these monitor windows, two between each pair of main studs spaced equally apart. Strap iron window bracket "S" used to make windows adjustable.

Rafters and balance of frame not already stated are of 2x4s. Roosts "R" are 2x3s on 2x4 cleats to swing up. Drop board is 2½ ft. above top of sill and is supported on a frame of 2x3s with 2x3 posts to floor. Door, to hinge at rear and open out is shown at "D". Windows, two full windows of 2 half-sash 8x12 glass, one on each side of door are shown at "W,W". The always-open-front, covered only by quarter-inch square mesh galvanized wire netting is shown at "O" and is approximately 4½ ft. by the width of house. At bottom of front is shown a 10 in. board from bottom of sill. Balance of front open except for studs and plate. The nests under dropping board are shown in dotted lines "N".

Fig. 80 shows floor plan of the 24x24 house and locates furnishings. Compass indicates that house faces due south. The black squares indicate the location of studding, also posts supporting girder for drop board. The black squares "A,A" as mentioned in foregoing, locate the main studs and the 4x4 studs supporting roof girder. Location of door "D", windows "W". Roosts are located as indicated in plan, nests are shown in dotted lines below dropping board. If additional nests are required they can be placed at convenient points on side walls.

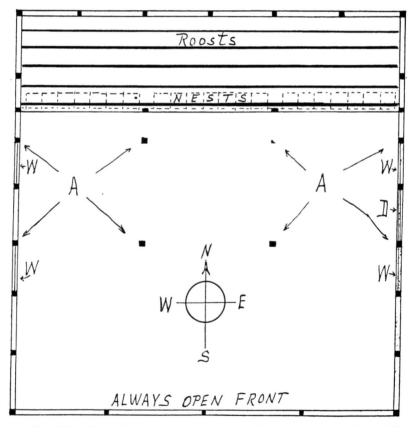

Fig. 80—The 200-Hen House. Floor plan and furnishing detail 24x24 semi-monitor house. Black squares show location of studs. See text.

On top of end and main studs in Fig. 79 the roof plates are shown in black; the plate for rear end of front rafters is shown at "P". These plates are 2x4s and support the rafters. The rafters are 2x4s and are spaced about 3 ft. apart at centers. They should be only lightly notched at ends and not at all where they rest on roof girder "T". It is a mistake to notch timbers too much for each bit cut out weakens the timber. The rear rafters are 16½ ft. long; front rafters 10 ft. 8 in. long.

In house plans the essential items are floor dimensions, height of building and proportions of front and rear sections. Also location of roosts in relation to door, windows and open-front. The frame detail can be varied a good deal to suit the views of individual builders and there is a wide variance of opinion on this matter. The building material will depend very largely upon the purse of the builder and the available supply. Often there is an opportunity to get good material at low cost from building wreckers.

This house makes up well with shingled sides and roof, or with sides of novelty siding, shiplap, or matched boards and roof of boards covered with good roofing fabric or metal roofing. Consult local builders and dealers about building material.

House for 500 Layers

The owners of this big 50x50 ft. semi-monitor open-front house say that it has given satisfaction thru two winters and one summer (reported spring of 1923). The rated capacity is 400 of the heavy breeds, or 500 Leghorns. Nearer 600 Leghorns were housed in it the first season, but it would be well to make 500 the limit.

This house is built on a concrete foundation and has a concrete floor. The sills are 4x6 timbers, treated with asphaltum, laid six-inch side up on foundation and bolted to it. Fig. 81 shows frame plan and detail of east side elevation. Application of the scale shown in plan will indicate position of framing material and dimensions.

The studs at front and back are 6 ft. from sill to plate "P", the corner studs are 4x4s, balance 2x4s. The big posts at either side of double doors are 6x6s, while timber at top of door is a 4x4. The door space is 8 ft. wide by 9 ft. high, and is closed by large double doors which open out. This gives ample space to drive into the house with a farm wagon when desired. At "A and A'" are shown 2x8 timbers spiked to front and back of main studs to serve as roof plates for rear of front rafters and to stiffen building. At "B and B'" are shown 4x4 roof girders running entire width of house

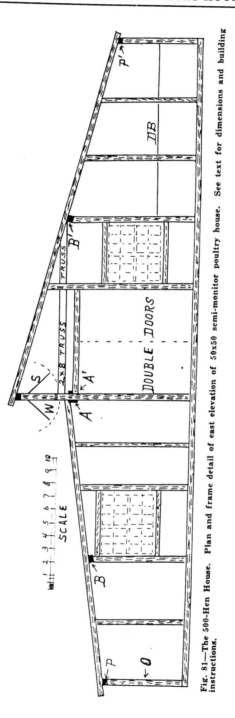

Fig. 81—The 500-Hen House. Plan and frame detail of east elevation of 50x50 semi-monitor poultry house. See text for dimensions and building instructions.

which support middle of rafters of front and back roof respectively. The studs under these girders are 4x6s, as also are balance of main studs except post at left of door. Balance of studs are 2x4s. The main studs are 13½ ft. long from sill to plate. The plates at top of main stud and end studs, shown in black, are 4x4s. A 2x8 truss is shown above door extending from main stud to rear rafter at a point just below level of window in monitor; there are four such trusses, one from each main stud except at sides of building. The rafters are only lightly notched to engage plates. They are of 2x4 stock and are laid two inch side up about 3 ft. to centers. The rear rafters are 30 ft. long. The front rafters are 23 ft. long.

The floor measure of this house is 50x50 ft. sill lines. Overall heights, approximately, 7 ft. front and rear, 15 ft. at peak of monitor, 10½ ft. at rear of front roof.

Large windows are used in east and west sides as indicated in dotted lines in Fig. 81. These windows carry 24 lights of 8x12 glass each and occupy a space of appriximately 4½x4½ ft. each. Bottom of window about 2 ft. 4 in. above sill. These large windows open at top and bottom. Location of dropping board is shown at "DB", 3 ft. above sill.

In the monitor there are 15 half sash windows, each about 2 ft. 4 in. x 2 ft. 3 in. and each having six lights 8x12 in. glass. Three of these half-sash windows, spaced equally apart, between each pair of main studs. Window sill and studs at sides of windows made of 2x4s. These monitor windows hinge at top to swing out and are fitted with adjustable strap-iron rods or brackets (See Chapters II and VI). Back of monitor windows are screens of inch-mesh netting on light frames, hinged at top to swing in. The four large side windows are also protected with screens on frames on inside.

The always-open-front at "O" is open from sill to plate entire width of house and covered only with quarter-inch square mesh galvanized wire netting, giving an open front, except for studs, of 6x50 ft.

Fig. 82 shows floor plan and furnishing detail of the 50x50 ft. house. The black squares on sill line indicate position of studs. Rear row of black squares on open floor locates the 4x6 studs supporting girder of rear roof. Middle row of black squares shows location of 4x6 main studs which support monitor. Front row of black squares on floor shows location of 4x6 studs supporting girder for front roof.

Water fountains are grouped on two platforms around two

middle studs under front roof girder. Mash hoppers "H,H" are built around two main studs under monitor as shown. The location of double doors is shown at "D". Side windows "W,W,W,W".

The nests "N,N" are arranged in banks on side walls, four tiers deep, bottom of lower nests about 2 ft. above top of sill. In the west bank there are 60 nests; in the east bank 28 nests. For heavy breeds a poultry ladder can be rigged for upper tiers of nests, tho it is seldom necessary.

The roosts are arranged above the dropping board as indicated at rear of house. The dropping board is 3 ft. above sills. Fig. 83 gives detail of roosts and dropping board. The roosts are 2x3s dovetailed at each end to engage the notches in front supports and in a rear string piece of 2x4 spiked to rear studs. Similar roosts

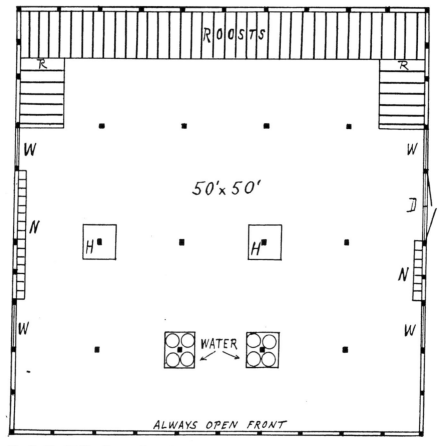

Fig. 82—The 500-Hen House. Floor plan and furnishing detail of 50x50 semi-monitor open-front poultry house for big flock units. Black squares show location of studs. See text.

are described in Chapters IV and V. These roosts lift out easily for cleaning. Each roost is 5 ft. 8 in. long.

In Fig. 83 the detail of roost ends is shown as seen from the top. Roosts in position are shown at "R", the dropping board at "DB", 2x4 girder under dropping board and one of posts "P" supporting same. The front roost supports "S,S" are 1x5 in. planed stock 8 in. long, which, when roost is notched in, brings bottom of roosts about 3 in. from dropping board. This arrangement of the roosts provides comfortable sleeping quarters and prevents crowding. With the large number of short roosts all the same distance from wall, there is no hogging of the rear roosts. Crowding immediately puts the end bird off the roost, with the result that the flock, especially a large flock, divides up better at night. As the roosts lift out and fit back again quickly, cleaning the drop board is comparatively easy.

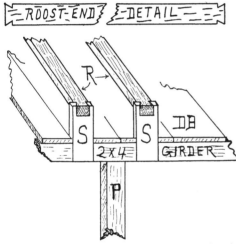

Fig. 83—Roost and Dropping Board Detail for the 50x50 big flock house. See text for description and dimensions.

The entire floor space below drop board is free for exercise and scratching space and gets ample light. Whole arrangement of interior of house is designed to keep all possible floor space free and to admit light and air to all parts.

The floor is kept supplied with sand and litter which is renewed as often as necessary. The dropping board requires frequent cleaning. As the big double doors readily admit a horse and wagon, cleaning and change of litter is more easily accomplished.

Positively **no curtains** of any sort used in this house. The front stays open the year 'round. The monitor windows are opened wide in summer and opened a few inches on all mild days in winter.

The sides and roof are boarded in with common boards and covered with corrugated metal roofing. Sides of rabbeted siding or shiplap and a roof covered with asbestos shingles should serve well and make an attractive house if kept painted. Covering roof and sides with good roofing fabric, substantially put on, would probably serve but might cost more in the end. If roof is to be covered with wood shingles it should have more pitch as it is a little flat. In sections where there is a great deal of snow in winter I would want to raise the height of monitor about 2 ft. and give each roof considerably more pitch.

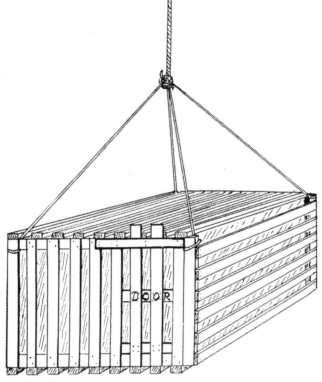

Fig. 84—A Good Old-Fashioned Breaking-up Coop for broody hens. Hangs from rafter or girder in house or from a limb of a tree in sheltered place. Size 3x3x2 ft. See text.

Personally I feel that such large houses are still in the experimental stage and are not suited to many localities. As before stated I much prefer the smaller flock unit and houses of the 24x24, 20x20 and 10x16 sizes. The 20x20 is a very satisfactory house and the 10x16 is always convenient.

Breaking-Up Coop for Broodies

No poultry house equipment is complete without a good breaking-up coop for broody hens. If they are taken the first night found on nest and put in such a coop, they break up quickly and laying is interrupted only for a very short period. Even the "non-sitting" Leghorns become broody, desire to sit, and often can be induced to hatch and rear a brood, as any keeper of large flocks knows.

Fig. 84 shows one of the oldest and best types of breaking-up coops that I know of. I do not know who was the originator. I have used coops like this for at least 40 years and think I got the plan originally from H. H. Stoddard or from some English poultry paper in boyhood days. No matter who first designed it, the coop is a good one for the purpose.

Anyone after looking over Fig. 84 should be able to build one of these breaking-up coops. The dimensions are 3x3 ft. floor measure and 2 ft. high. It will be noted that the floor is slatted with 1x2 in. stuff. Whole coop is made slatted with 1x2 in. stock, preferably spruce, redwood or some tough material.

The door at one end, as indicated, is the common sliding door for poultry crates, and slips up and down. The coop is slung with rope from all four corners of top, centering in a single large rope with knotted end.

For winter use the coop can be suspended from rafter, roof girder, or wherever wanted, at convenient height to be easily reached and yet out of the way. In summer I sling mine in a shady spot from the limb of a large pine tree, out of view from highway and high enough to be safe.

So slung this breaking-up coop swings and tilts as the fowls move about. They cannot sit and must roost on slatted bottom. They are watered but not fed often. If very fat they get food every other day, otherwise once a day and only a little hard grain.

Usually, if taken early, the most persistent Asiatics will be cured of broodiness by from three to five days' confinement in this coop. The longer they are allowed to remain on nest the longer it takes to cure them and the longer it takes to get back to egg producing.

Try one of these breaking-up coops for your flock and you will never return to the bothersome and unsatisfactory methods so often recommended for breaking up broodies.

Do not overcrowd the breaking-up coop. If there are many broodies do not put more into the coop than it will carry with comfort. Ten or a dozen hens make a full coop. If more must be accommodated, provide other breaking-up coops. If they show a disposition to return to the nests when released, put them back in coop for a few days more.

CHAPTER XII

Why Open-Front is Better Than the Closed House—Beneficial Results from Fresh Air—Best for Fowls in All Climates—Conditioning and Training Quarters—Special Equipment for Fanciers—Plans and Instructions for Building a Good Dependable ITrapnest

"Poultry require FRESH AIR, SUNLIGHT, DRYNESS, and ROOM. Of these by far the most important is fresh air. The essential condition of dryness depends much upon free circulation of fresh air. Air and sunlight are Nature's best disinfectants and germicides, and if a coop or house is not overcrowded, and the birds are in normal, healthy condition, a properly aired and sunned structure requires much less attention to cleanliness than one that is deficient in these particulars."—John H. Robinson in "Principles and Practice of Poultry Culture."

IN THE PRECEDING chapters are given plans and descriptions of several different types of desirable open-front or fresh-air poultry houses and also certain equipment for applying modern fresh-air methods to chick rearing.

As only a limited number of illustrations could be used, these plans were selected from a great many different types of buildings which are giving their owners satisfactory results. If your favorite fresh-air house has not been included in this selection that does not mean that it is not approved of as a good and desirable house. There are many other types of open-front poultry houses, some excellent and some not so good.

The essential thing for every poultry keeper, who desires to get the best results from his flocks, is to adopt some good dependable type of always-open-front poultry house and give his fowls the benefits of living and sleeping under practically open-air conditions.

Many authorities and successful poultrymen have been quoted and reports of experience introduced proving the necessity for, the desirability and the beneficial effects of, fresh-air poultry housing. If the reader still remains unconvinced concerning the value and safety of open-front poultry houses, continues to be opposed to fresh-air housing, or, making a half-hearted attempt, does not give such modern buildings a fair trial, I can only say with Butler:

"He that complies against his will,
Is of his own opinion still,
Which he may adhere to, yet disown,
For reasons to himself best known."

Why Open-Front Is Better

Summarizing the evidence already presented herewith are a dozen reasons why the open-front poultry house is better than the closed type. The semi-monitor type of open-front poultry house possesses these advantages:

1. It supplies an abundance of fresh-air at all times, day and night, particularly at night when much needed.

2. Plenty of sunshine and light penetrate practically all parts of the house.

3. High windows in monitor admit sunlight to rear of house.

4. It is a dry house, having free circulation of air at all times.

5. There is more room for the fowls.

6. The floor space is less obstructed.

7. It is more comfortable than a closed house. .

8. An open-front is more humane than the closed building.

9. Fowls prefer the open-front house.

10. Easy to care for and keep clean. Practically "fool proof."

11. Not expensive to build.

12. Simple in construction, a novice can build one.

Beneficial Results of Fresh-Air

The benefits which the poultry and their owner derive from open-front housing and fresh-air methods of caring for poultry of all ages are many. These beneficial results of fresh-air living may be summed up as follows:

1. Both chicks and fowls enjoy better health.

2. They are more vigorous and hardy.

3. They possess greater vitality.

4. They have greater power to resist disease.

5. The pullets and hens produce more eggs.

6. Eggs show a higher percentage fertility.

7. The eggs hatch better.

8. Better, strong, hardy, livable chicks.

9. Birds of all ages are less affected by weather changes.

10. There is less danger of frosted combs and wattles.

11. The birds have better and more lustrous plumage with finer texture and better color.

12. Fresh-air flocks do not consume any more food than closed-house flocks and they make better use of their food.

Open-Air Living Best for Fowls

The plumage of fowls prevents loss of body heat and insulates them against heat and cold. Nature provides a new suit of feathers and heavy underfluff for winter weather. Fowls cannot lay aside their overcoats and heavy underwear at will, they wear their clothing continuously until part is shed with the approach of warm weather and the entire suit is renewed in the fall before settled cold weather is established. If they are confined in warm houses, or frequently exposed to extreme changes of temperature, such as a house overwarm by day and very cold at night, or running in and out of a warm house when the outdoor temperature is cold, they are uncomfortable and in danger of "catching colds."

In addition to being always heavily clothed, fowls normally have a much higher temperature than man. The normal temperature of man is 98.6 degrees F. and comparatively slight variations may indicate serious trouble. In a careful study of the temperature of fowls, Dr. B. F. Kaupp found a wide range of variation under apparently normal conditions. The temperature range, in examining a number of apparently healthy hens of several breeds under varying conditions, was from 103.2 in case of one individual to 110.8 in another. In a series of tests in 1917 with 48 fowls the average temperature was 106.6. The average normal temperature for fowls, from all studies to date of August 1922, was 107.4 degrees F. In discussion of his temperature tests Dr. Kaupp says:

"The temperatures of these fowls were highest at night, gradually becoming lower after the fowl goes to perch till at midnight all surplus heat from the body is apparently eliminated and the average fell to 104.5 degrees F. Nearing dawn the birds become restless and soon begin to move about, which causes surplus heat to accumulate in the body. At this time the average temperature was 105.7. From this time till noon the temperature gradually rose to 106.6 and by 5 p. m. had reached 106.9 * * * * *.

"From all studies recorded it would appear that 107.4 degrees F. is an annual approximate temperature, while this is likely to be slightly more during warmer and less during colder weather."

With a normally high range of temperature and with rapid variations, which accommodate the individual to climatic and atmospheric changes and to the needs of rest and exercise, it should be obvious that Nature has fitted fowls for open-air living.

Study of the anatomy and physiology of fowls reveals many other reasons why open-air living is best for them, the peculiar structure of the organs of respiraton and of the skin, the fact that fowls live rapidly and breathe rapidly, and that they need vastly more oxygen in proportion to their weight than does man, and so on thru a long list of reasons—most of which have been mentioned in preceding chapters—which demonstrate that Nature made fowls to live in the open and that housing them is an artificial plan for the convenience of man.

Important for Fanciers

Some say, "The open-front poultry houses are all well enough for egg farmers, market poultrymen and other practical poultry keepers with large or small flocks, but they are not suited to the requirements of fanciers who breed show birds and some delicate varieties." That is an error.

Fig. 85—Conditioning and training house used by F. H. Thomas, breeder of "Fayette" White Wyandottes, Connersville, Ind. See text.

Above all else the fancier needs healthy breeding stock possessing the maximum of constitutional vigor. The so-called delicate breeds would no longer be delicate if bred for health and properly cared for under fresh-air conditions from shell to showroom. I have bred and reared Dorkings and also White Faverolles—a bearded and crested variety—under the same fresh-air conditions as other supposedly more hardy varieties, with splendid results and improvement in health and vigor. Houdans, Polish, Hamburgs and Minorcas respond well to fresh-air methods. I believe that any breed or variety can be bred for

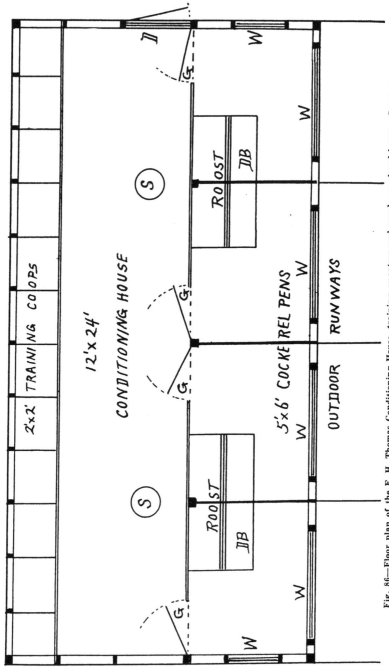

Fig. 86—Floor plan of the F. H. Thomas Conditioning House, training quarters and surplus cockerel house. See text.

health under fresh-air conditions and so improved in health and hardiness in a few seasons, that they will be able to resist disease and need no longer be considered delicate. Coddling and pampering chicks and fowls, keeping them in warm tight quarters, fussing over them with every change of the weather, all with the mistaken notion that such treatment is being kind to them and protecting them, is very largely responsible for certain breeds and varieties being kept in the "delicate" class. Common sense fresh-air methods combined with intelligent breeding and feeding for health, and seasoning and hardening of both young and old stock, will work wonders for any breed or variety.

Some of our leading fanciers, men who have earned the title of "master breeders," use open-front houses and employ fresh-air methods and are getting better and better results. Each season fresh-air recruits more and more to the ranks of the successful. All of the twelve beneficial results of fresh-air methods tabulated above are essential to the continued success of fanciers.

For All Climates

Modern fresh-air poultry houses are desirable and necessary for all climates. They are particularly needed in climates where the winters are very cold and severe storms frequent. In warm climates fowls require little more than a roofed shelter with sufficient side walls to break the prevailing high winds.

As is pointed out in "Directions for Living and Sleeping in the Open Air," for prevention, treatment and cure of certain diseases of human beings, by Thomas Spees Carrington, M. D., "What is of most importance is to find a sheltered spot protected from the wind, for the wind is much harder to bear than even intense cold."

Dr. Carrington also emphasizes the importance of breathing air that is fresh and pure, eating an abundance of good food, avoiding worry and over much strenuous exercise, and the need of ample rest and sleep, and says, "Live out of doors. This means that as many hours of the day and night as possible should be spent in the open air, and in order to carry out this treatment some place must be provided which is not only protected from wind, but also from rain and snow."

For poultry the deep house of semi-monitor type with an always-open front provides ample protection from wind, drafts, and storms. Such houses have been proved successful and wholly satisfactory in severe northern climates where the temperature is often at zero or below and where on extremely cold nights the temperature may drop to 30 or even 40 degrees below zero. See testimony in preceding chapters.

The deep house is needed where winters are severe. The shallow open-front house works very well in mild climates and good results have been secured with such in locations where the winters are severe. Depth, as applied to poultry houses, is largely a relative term and it should be proportionate to width and height of open front. A house 6 ft. wide by 10 ft. deep, of semi-monitor open-front type, is a deep house. A shed-roofed house 40 ft. wide by 12 ft. deep, is a shallow house. A 10x16 semi-monitor house is deep, so are the 20x20, 24x24 and 50x50 houses. All things considered the deep houses are preferable and have many advantages over shallow buildings.

Conditioning and Cockerel House

In March 1923, a letter to the publishers from F. H. Thomas, breeder of "Fayette" White Wyandottes, Connersville, Ind., says:

"I have been reading with a great deal of interest Dr. Woods' notes on his fresh air houses. I have been using this type house for several years and like it fine. I have put one of these houses to a use that I never heard of anyone else trying. In the front of the house I have four pens, 5x6 ft., with runs out front. In these pens I keep my surplus males and in the rear I have a double tier of training coops. In these coops I can coop 24 single birds at one time. I have used this house for several years for a conditioning house and have conditioned as many as 40 birds at one time. It is easy to heat and with the perfect ventilation birds will dry, after they have been washed, much faster than they will in the ordinary house."

I wrote to Mr. Thomas for a photograph of this house and a pencil sketch of plans. Fig. 85 shows photographic view of this conditioning and cockerel house as used by him. In this building which is 12x24 ft., cellar window sashes are used for the monitor windows and six 9-light windows are used to close the open-front. These front windows, provided because the house is used as conditioning quarters where white birds are washed and dried, run in grooves and slide out at side, permitting any adjustment desired. The small poultry doors into run are under the windows.

In drawing the plans for this house I have made a slight modification in the front which I think improves it. The dimensions are the same otherwise. Instead of sliding windows I have provided swing or tilting windows slung on pivot at center, to swing in at top and out at bottom. The poultry door into run can be provided for at side of window.

As manner of framing such buildings has been covered at length in Chapter VI and others following, I will not go into details about it here. Fig. 86 shows floor plan of the Thomas Conditioning House and location of out-door runs is indicated. This house is 12 ft. deep by 24 ft. wide. The location of studding is indicated in black squares, windows "W", door "D". Along the rear wall are 24 training coops, each 2x2 ft., arranged in two tiers. In front of these coops is liberal open floor space for work in washing and conditioning specimens for sale or show-room. Two brooder stoves "S,S" from which stovepipe goes up thru cast-iron flanged chimney piece set in roof (such can be obtained of supply dealers) supply the heat to dry out washed birds. Monitor and front windows can be adjusted to secure perfect ventila-·tion.

The pens for surplus cockerels, as shown, come under lower front roof. There are four of these pens, each 5 ft. deep by 6 ft. wide and provided with a roost and drop board "DB" as shown. Gates "G" are provided in wire partition at back of pens. All furnishings should be made portable and easily removable, including partitions and roosts, etc. The door is in east end and there is a small four-light window in each end as shown.

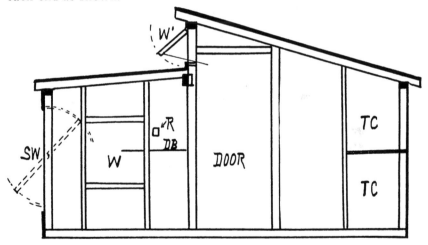

Fig. 87—End elevation and frame plan of F. H. Thomas Conditioning House. See text.

Fig. 87 shows east end elevation and frame plan of this conditioning house. It is 12 ft. deep, high section is 7 ft. deep and low section 5 ft. Overall heights are 5 ft. 3 in. at rear wall; 7 ft. 3 in. at front of monitor; 5 ft. 6 in. at rear of front roof; monitor is 1 ft. 9 in.; front is 5 ft. The front is boarded up 10 inches at bottom and down 8 in. at top. There are four swing or pivoted windows "SW" each 4 ft. wide by 3 ft. 3 in. high. These windows swing in at top and out at bottom as indicated by dotted lines. To protect the opening, quarter-

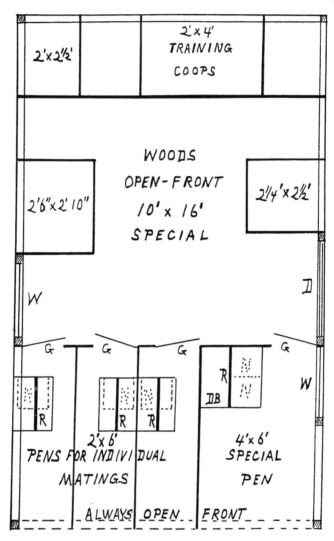

Fig. 88—Woods 10x16 open-front house floor plan with special furnishings for training coops and pens for small matings.

inch square mesh galvanized wire netting can be used for upper half of window on outside and lower half on inside of front. A small 2x2 ft., 4-light window "W" occupies same location in each end. Roost "R" and dropping board "DB" in cockerel pens are located in plan. Monitor window "W'" is a 3-light cellar window sash, hinged at top to open out and adjustable by a strap-iron bracket as in other semi-monitor houses. There are five of these monitor windows spaced equally apart. The double tier of training coops is shown at "TC."

This Thomas Conditioning House is a good and convenient building for the purpose and should give excellent results. The windows should not be kept too tightly closed, as a good circulation of air without drafts is necessary when drying washed birds.

Special Equipment for 10x16

Several of our fancier friends want plans for converting a Woods Open-front House into training quarters and pens for small and individual or single pair matings. I do not like to cramp fowls by confining them in too small pens. In a 10x16 ft. house 40 fowls, with an allowance of 4 sq. ft. floor space each, are comfortable enough, but two fowls in a pen 2x6, with 6 sq. ft. floor room each are rather cramped for space to move about in. For a small pen my preference would be to provide 6x10 houses as described in Chapter VIII. However, there are many times when small pens under one roof are needed.

Fig. 88 shows the furnishing of a 10x16 ft. open-front to supply convenient training coops and small pens. In this floor plan the sill outlines are shown, windows "W", door "D". There are two tiers of training coops at rear of house, six singles 2 ft x 2½ ft. and two large pens 2x4 ft. each. On east side, one above the other, are two pens 2¼x2½ ft. each and on west side two pens each 2 ft. 6 in. by 2 ft. 10 in. In the low front section are three 2x6 ft. pens for individual or single pair matings and one special pen 4x6 ft. Gates "G" are indicated in wire partition. Drop boards "DB" are located in outline with nests "N" under same and roosts "R" above boards. All of these fittings should be made portable and easily removable. Partitions can be made on frames and fastened in with hooks or iron buttons.

Fig. 89 shows outline plan of east end elevation of this 10x16 house. The overall heights differ a little from usual dimensions, front is 6 ft. high; peak 10 ft. 9 in.; monitor 3 ft. 2 in.; rear of front roof 7 ft. 7 in.; rear of house 5 ft. 11 in. In other respects this house is the regular 10x16 open-front semi-monitor house and the reader is referred to Chapter VI for plans and general instructions for building. Monitor window "W" hinges at top to swing out. The always-open-front is indicated at "O". The opening is 4 ft. 2 in. high by width of house and covered only with quarter-inch square mesh galvanized wire netting. No curtains of any kind used. The front is boarded up 10 inches from bottom of sill and down 8 inches from plate at top. The small matings housed so near the open-front will not suffer any ill effects nor will they be unduly exposed. The winter of 1922-23 was uncommonly severe. I had a number of birds cooped even closer to the wire front and they wintered well.

Personally I would not hesitate to sling a canopy brooder hover from middle of rear roof to supply heat and use this house to wash birds without closing the front. Have not tried it, but I did use such a brooder to heat house for a farrowing pig and altho weather was

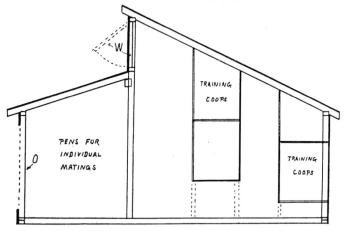

Fig. 89—End elevation outline of 10x16 semi-monitor open-front house with special furnishings for training coops and pens for small matings. See text.

severely cold the sow and her little pigs did famously without any losses. And new-born pigs are far more delicate than wet fowls. In two 10x16s we had flocks which ran to the weather all winter and frequently the fowls were drenched by running about in the cold rain. They dried out on the roost at night without any heat other than that supplied by their own bodies and some of the nights were severely cold. No colds and not even a wet nostril resulted; the birds remained in perfect health. Nature seems to know her business.

I do not advise nor recommend that anyone attempt to condition fowls by washing in an open-front house. The Thomas Conditioning House, Fig. 86, seems to fill the requirements of a good house for this purpose. While fowls, in all probability, would not suffer any ill effects they need to become accustomed to a closed building before being sent to the show room—to be tapered off or to gradually become

Fig. 90—Simple Trap Nests in use under dropping board. See text. Photo by courtesy of the U. S. Department of Agriculture.

used to being confined in a partially closed and heated building. Man, beast, or fowl having, thru habit, become accustomed to living and sleeping in the open air suffers keenly thru lessening of the supply of fresh air in closed quarters. After sleeping out of doors for a long period the first night in a closed sleeping room is misery, as I can testify from personal experience; also it is decidedly uncomfortable for one accustomed to outdoor living to travel in stuffy ill-ventilated cars. So, just as it is necessary to train fowls to pose well in training or exhibition coops, it is desirable to train them to look and appear at their best in a conditioning house that approximates show room conditions before the birds are shipped to the show.

A Good Dependable Trap Nest

A trap nest is a nest for layers that traps the hen after she enters it to lay and she cannot get out again until released by the attendant, who makes a record of her leg band number and date on the egg and checks the egg on her individual laying record. Trap nest records are very useful in breeding and are necessary for pedigree breeding, unless one resorts to single pair matings. Attending the nests and keeping the records makes a great deal of extra work, but there are many breeders who believe that it pays, tho some trap nest their birds for only part of the year.

At least three trap nests are required for any small flock and for flocks of from 20 to 25 layers provide one trap nest for each four hens.

The most satisfactory trap nest I have used is the simple trap nest recommended by the U. S. Department of Agriculture in Farmers' Bulletin No. 682, July 9, 1915. This nest may be attached to side walls of poultry house or to underside of the dropping board with front facing out. Fig. 90 shows a bank of three of Uncle Sam's trap nests located underneath the dropping board. The right and left nests are sprung and occupied by layers. The middle nest is set ready to trap a layer.

"When the hen enters this nest her back raises the door "c" (Fig. 91) which releases the catch of trigger 'a' and allows the door to shut. The catch should be set so that its edge just holds the door, which position is regulated by a screw or nail at lower inside edge of catch. A washer should be placed on the screw 'd' between the catch and the side of nest to prevent this catch from sticking. The guard 'b' around the catch keeps the nesting material away from the catch. The length of the catch which supports the door and the triangular notch in the door may be varied slightly for very small or very large hens." This paragraph and the directions for construction of a bank of three nests which follows are quoted from the farmers' bulletin which was prepared by Alfred R. Lee.

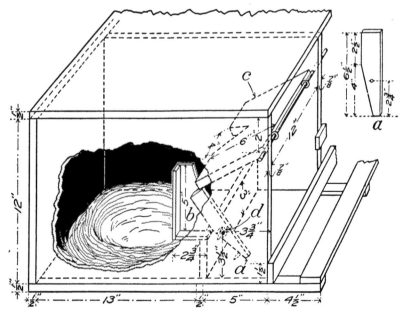

Fig. 91—Working plans for Simple Trap Nest. See text. Plans by courtesy of U. S. Department of Agriculture.

Directions for Constructing Trap Nest

"Cut four ⅞-inch boards for ends and partitions, 12 inches wide by 19 inches long, enough ½-inch boards 39½ inches long, laid lengthwise, to cover the top, back, and bottom, and one strip 39½ inches long and 1½ inches wide for the front of the nests. Cut three pieces of ½-inch boards 12 inches long and 3 inches high to insert in the nest to hold the nesting material away from the door.

"Nail the top, back, and bottom to the ends and partitions (see Fig. 91), insert the 3-inch strips in the nests, and make the guard 'b', nailing it to the left side of the nest. Bore a hole in the catch 'a' large enough so that the catch will move freely when screwed into position on the side. Place a washer on the screw between the catch and the side of the nest. Place a screw at the lower edge of the catch to stop it when set, so that the catch will just hold the door.

"Make the doors 'c' of ⅞-inch material, 12 inches by 6 inches, and cut a triangular notch 4 inches wide in center of lower edge. Put two screw-eyes in the top of the doors and bore holes in the front of the nests 2 inches below the top (inside measurement), thru which a 3-16 inch wire is run to support the doors.

"Attach a narrow strip to the front of the nests for the hens to jump upon when entering nests. Place a button or block of wood on the front of each partition to hold the door when nest is closed."

Red cedar or redwood makes the best material for building this trap nest. For use under the dropping board it may be made with a slatted top. I much prefer to use these nests in tiers attached to the side walls of the house. When so used the nests should have a solid top and the uppermost nests should have a sharp slant to top to prevent fowls roosting upon them.

Conclusion

Tho open-front poultry houses have been boosted thru two decades, are in successful use in great numbers all over the American Continent and in some foreign lands, there may yet be found a few who vigorously oppose the use of open-front fresh-air poultry houses and who seem unable to discuss the subject without getting angry.

In closing let me suggest to the reader, when he meets such a "constitutional objector" to open-front poultry houses, that he bear in mind that famous line of Haliburton:

"When a man is wrong and won't admit it, he always gets angry."

(The End)

ALSO FROM NORTON CREEK PRESS

POULTRY

Success With Baby Chicks by Robert Plamondon. A complete guide to hatchery selection, mail-order chicks, day-old chick care, brooding, brooder plans, feeding, and housing.

Feeding Poultry by G. F. Heuser. The classic guide to poultry nutrition for chickens, turkeys, ducks, geese, gamebirds, and pigeons.

Genetics of the Fowl by F. B. Hutt. The classic guide to chicken genetics and poultry breeding.

The Dollar Hen by Milo M. Hastings. The classic guide to American free-range egg farming.

BACK TO THE LAND

Ten Acres Enough: Small-Farm Self-Sufficiency Through High-Quality Produce by Edmund Morris. A back-to-the-land adventure from 1864.

Gold in the Grass: Rags to Riches Through Soil Reclamation and Sustainable Farming by Margaret Leatherbarrow. A Back-to-the-land adventure from 1954.

We Wanted a Farm by M. G. Kains. A back-to-the-land adventure by the author of *Five Acres and Independence*.

New old titles are being released constantly! Visit our site at http://www.nortoncreekpress.com for more information.

Poultryman's View After Eight Years' Successful Use of Semi-monitor House

East Haven, Conn., Dec. 11, 1922
Dr. Prince T. Woods,
Silver Lake, Mass.

Dear Sir:—Enclosed please you will find a clipping from "N. E. Homestead" that I thought might interest you.

I am using a semi-monitor type house 22x36 for the last 8 years and I FIND IT BETTER THAN ANY OTHER TYPE AND I DON'T FIND ANY OF THE FAULTS NAMED.   Respectfully yours,
(Signed)   J. B. TOMAN.

(Note.—Here is a man who has used the house successfully eight years and finds it better than any other type. I do not recall that I ever met this poultryman and I have never visited his plant, yet practical everyday use of the house has made him sufficiently interested to send me the clipping named and to give the semi-monitor type house a splendid endorsement. —P. T. W.)

In Cold Quebec

Writing the last of March, 1911, J. W. Dunfield, Kingsbury, Quebec, Canada, says of the Woods open-front colony houses, "I have had two in use during the last winter in 'cold and stormy Quebec.' It has been the coldest and stormiest winter in many years, so the houses have had a very thoro tryout, and have given excellent satisfaction in every way. The thermometer has been down to 35 degrees below zero four nights this winter, and as low as 20 to 25 degrees below at least eight or ten other nights. * * * * I consider the Woods house to be the best I have yet tried. * * * The health of all the birds has been excellent, but the birds in the Woods houses have a more glossy plumage."

(Note.—Canadian users find the Woods house a dry and comfortable house. Most of them prefer to use a dropping board below the roost. Some use "snow fences" near the houses to keep big drifts away from front of poultry houses.—P. T. W.)

Successful Farmer Voices Protest —Used Woods House Since 1908—Likes It

Danvers, Mass., Jan. 5th, 1923.
Dr. Prince T. Woods,
Silver Lake, Mass.

Dear Doctor:—I want to protest the knock on Woods house (semi-monitor type) in Dec. 9 "New England Homestead" in which the editor says, "It is about the poorest proposition for a poultry house we have seen," and goes on to find theoretical faults with it. Evidently he has no practical knowledge of this house.

I have used the Woods or semi-monitor open-front house since 1908. I HAVE NOT FOUND ANY OF THE FAULTS THIS EDITOR NAMES.

The construction of the Woods house admits of it being built of lighter material than other types, therefore it is less expensive. A friend of mine has just built a 20x20 ft. house of this type at a cost of $110, a first cost for housing capacity of only $1.10 per hen. Not too expensive?

I know another poultryman who is located in a very damp section of Massachusetts and he tells me that HE FINDS LESS DAMPNESS IN THE WOODS HOUSE THAN IN ANY OTHER, and he has four different types of houses.

This will make the fifteenth winter that I have used the Woods house and found it always warm and comfortable as compared with other poultry houses. There is bound to be good circulation of air with even distribution of light and sunshine thru the whole house. My experience has been that the house is absolutely without drafts. I think the Woods semi-monitor type poultry house too good a house to be thrown down and that is why I am writing this letter.   Yours truly,
(Signed)   JOHN W. DWINELL.

(Note.—Mr. Dwinell is a successful farmer and poultryman. He has one of the first Woods houses built. It is located on an exposed hillside where the winters are cold and the snow deep.—P. T. W.)

Editor's Theoretical Objections "Monitor Type Hen House"

Q.—"What do you think of the half-monitor house type for a hen house?"
A.—"It is about the poorest proposition for a poultry house that we have seen. It is very expensive because it contains two roofs and two fronts, and must be supported quite substantially on account of the heavy weight of the upper front. It is usually a cold house in winter as the heat radiates thru the glass in the upper front very rapidly. It is a damp house because as the heat will radiate thru the upper front, the moisture is trapped. If these upper windows are opened, the house will become extremely cold and drafty."—New England Homestead, Dec. 9, 1922.

Found in Advertising Matter

A circular advertising some well-known feeds carries an attractive illustration of Woods houses used at a state hospital, but in general remarks on housing says: "The half-monitor house has been quite successful in certain parts of the country, but probably not as generally successful as the shed roof or gable house. Its chief advantage lies in keeping the house cool in the summer, but it is usually a damp house in the winter."

(Note.—Here is more theory and no real experience. I must confess that I do not understand the reason for these "slams" and general statements condemning a house which, so evidently, the writer knows practically nothing about and has had no actual experience with. While it is often true that "every knock is a boost" and we all look for differences of opinion as a matter of course, why cannot these apparently "conscientious objectors," who really know so little about the subject yet assume so much, at least be fair and honest in stating their differences?—P. T. W.)

32919141R00110

Made in the USA
Middletown, DE
24 June 2016